M000080720

NICK PARSONS is a graduate of Sydney University (BA Philosophy), the Australian Film, Television and Radio School (BA Film and TV) and the National Institute of Dramatic Art (Diploma in directing). In 1994 Nick was resident director at NIDA.

He has directed more than a dozen stageplays including *Norm and Ahmed* (Griffin Theatre Co.), *The Visitor* (Griffin Theatre Co.), *The Removalists* (NIDA), *Handful of Friends* (NIDA) and *The Devils* (NIDA). He has directed two short films, *Little Horrors* and *The Portrait of Wendy's Father*. His writing credits include *Requiem* (AFTRS), *The Visitor* (Griffin Theatre Co.), *Pest House* and *Dead Heart* (stageplays for NIDA), *Lithium Cake* (ABC Radio) and *Heartland* (ABC TV). *Dead Heart* won the 1994 NSW Premier's Literary Award, an AWGIE Award, and the Australian Human Rights Award.

Dead Heart marks Nick Parsons' feature film directorial debut.

DEAD HEART

Original Screenplay by
Nick Parsons

Currency Press • Sydney

First published 1996 by
Currency Press Ltd,
PO Box 452, Paddington,
NSW 2021, Australia

10 9 8 7 6 5 4 3 2 1 0

Copyright © Nick Parsons 1996

This book is copyright. Apart from any fair dealing for the purpose of private study, research or review, as permitted under the Copyright Act, no part may be reproduced by any process without written permission. Inquiries concerning publication, translation or recording rights should be addressed to the publishers.
All rights to this film script are reserved and permission to reproduce any part must be obtained in advance from the author through the publishers.

NATIONAL LIBRARY OF AUSTRALIA CIP DATA
Parsons, Nicholas, 1961-.
    Dead heart : the screenplay
    ISBN 0 86819 459 X
    I. Title. II. Title: Dead heart (Motion picture).
791.4372

Printed by Southwood Press, Marrickville, NSW, Australia
Cover design by Susan Mikulic

PHOTOGRAPHIC ACKNOWLEDGMENTS: The production stills used on the front cover and appearing within the text were all taken by Lisa Tomasetti.

Front cover: Djunawong Stanley Mirindo as Tjulpu; p.i Nick Parsons; p.ii Tjulpu; p.vi Bryan Brown as Ray Lorkin; p.2 Billy McPherson as First Man, Gnarnayarrahe Waitaire as Poppy and David Gulpilil as Second Man; p.7 (above) Peter Francis as Mannga, Aaron Pedersen as Tony and Ernie Dingo as David; p.7 (below) Mannga, Ray, Lafe Charlton as Billy and David; p.12 Tony; p.24 Angie Milliken as Kate and Tony; p.28 (above) David; p.28 (below) Ray and David; p.59 (above) Mannga; p.59 (below) Ray and Tjulpu; p.86 (above) Ray; p.86 (below) Tjulpu; p.91 Kate, John Jarratt as Charlie, Lewis Fitz-Gerald as Les, (foreground) Courtnee Spessot as Sonia and Max Spessot as Adrian.

Contents

Foreword

Bryan Brown

I read a first draft of *Dead Heart* in late 1992. He'd given it to me after a meeting I'd had with a family friend of Nick's. He shyly presented me with the script saying he'd like me to read it with the idea of playing Ray Lorkin, the cop. Two things happened after I read it. Firstly I decided I didn't want anyone else to play the cop and secondly I was taken by the maturity of the story.

When I asked Nick who was to direct *Dead Heart* he said he was. He neglected to tell me he'd only made a nineteen-minute film before that. When asked who would produce it, he replied he didn't know. So I said I would. As it turned out Helen Watts produced it with me.

Well, a lot of red dirt has passed through the fingernails since then. Nick rewrote the screenplay as a stageplay and it was successful and then rewrote the screenplay.

During 1994 that screenplay went from 240 pages to 220, 180, 160, 140, 120 and finally to 109 pages. At that stage I thought it was filmable. The final screenplay is very different to the one I first read. It's richer. Nick learned a lot in his research for the play.

Nick will write many more screenplays. He's very talented. But I bet he'll look back on *Dead Heart* with more than just fondness. It's been quite a journey for him. And for me.

October 1996

A Plea for Understanding

David Stratton

On October 16, 1967, the world premiere of an Australian film was held at the Centre Cinema in Canberra. The Prime Minister, Harold Holt (a few weeks before his death), was guest of honour, and in the opening speeches, much was made of the fact that this was the first time a colour feature shot in this country had been processed in a local lab (and not sent overseas) and furthermore had been post-produced here. The film was *Journey Out of Darkness*, a drama set in the Dead Heart, in which a white police officer from Melbourne (played by an American actor, Konrad Matthaei) is sent to arrest an aborigine (played by a Sri Lankan singer, Kamahl) for a tribal murder The policeman is assisted by an aboriginal tracker, played by the white Australian actor Ed Devereux in chocolate makeup which made him look a bit like Al Jolson in *The Jazz Singer*. The film was the work of an American television director, James Trainor, and the evening was a severe embarrassment for all concerned.

Memories of that terrible night came back to me as I watched Nick Parson's powerful *Dead Heart,* which contains many of the same elements as *Journey Out of Darkness,* including the theme of the white policeman trying to come to terms with tribal aboriginal law. Needless to say, we've come a long way in the last twenty-nine years and, though some of the more ignorant members of our society, including the odd independent federal politician, would seemingly like to turn the clock back, films dealing with aboriginal themes will never look like *Journey Out of Darkness* again. Nevertheless, it's salutary to remember that, as recently as 1985, an Indian actress, Neela Day, played an aboriginal woman in Tim Burstall's adaptation of Morris West's novel, *The Naked Country*.

Dead Heart, which Parsons has adapted from his own award-winning play, has been in gestation for ten years; in 1986, Parsons, a graduate of the Australian Film Television and Radio School and of the National Institute of Dramatic Art, started working on the story as a screenplay, but turned it into a play when funding proved elusive. Perhaps the reason the finished product is so cinematic is because the material was originally conceived as a film.

The aboriginal characters in *Dead Heart* represent, I imagine, most strands of outback community life: the tribal elders, the rebellious youth, the western-educated priest, the ordinary battlers. Parsons explores their world, and that of the tiny township of Wala Wala, with candour and insight. His characters, black and white, are boldly conceived and intelligently developed and the drama which unfolds, while superficially similar to other filmed stories of white man's justice confronted by tribal law, is both original and dramatically satisfying.

The final film, flawlessly cast and strikingly photographed by James Bartle, could not have been made without the support and encouragement of Bryan Brown, one of this country's best, but often least-appreciated, actors. His portrayal of the cop who tries to come to terms with aboriginal justice and culture is one of his best.

As a heartfelt plea for friendship and understanding between Australia's original population and its more recent migrants, *Dead Heart* is, indeed, timely.

Leura, October 1996

Author's Note

Nick Parsons

Where the characters speak in dialect, the English follows immediately in small type, square brackets and quotes: ['Dialogue'].

I want to make it clear from the start that this is not an 'Aboriginal movie'. Although I have an interest in Aboriginal issues, I am not Aboriginal. This screenplay does not portray Aboriginal life and culture for its own sake. Rather, I have tried to show what happens when two cultures, with completely different values, come into conflict. My perspective is white, but I have tried to depict what I see as good and bad on both sides without prejudice or sentimentality.

An enormous contribution to the screenplay has been made by all those who assisted in the production of the stageplay *Dead Heart* by the NIDA Company which opened at the NIDA Theatre, Kensington, on 12 May 1993. Most particularly this includes the director, John Clark, and cast: Kevin Smith, John Jarratt, Glen Shea, Elaine Hudson, Ross Hall, Nicholas Garsden, Lance O'Chin, David Ngoombudjarra, Tom E. Lewis, Alan Dargin, Terry Brady, Jeanette Cronin.

The second production by Black Swan and Belvoir Street Theatre was no less valuable, and this includes particularly the director Neil Armfield, and cast: Steve Bisley, Mitchell Butel, Jack Charles, Peter Francis, Mort Hansen, Gillian Jones, Geoff Kelso, Angie Milliken, Stanley Mirindo, Dickon Oxenburgh, Trevor Parfitt, Kelton Pell, George Shevtsov, Kevin Smith (again) and Michael Watson.

On the film I was fortunate to work with a tremendous cast and crew too numerous to mention here, however their names are listed in the end credits of this book. Special mention must be made however of Bryan Brown, who produced, acted and, with

Joanna Arrowsmith, script edited *Dead Heart*. Many were the times I was convinced the script was right and we could do no better; yet Bryan's ruthless determination inevitably found a cut or an improvement. In fact, so efficient was he that of over seven hundred slates that were shot, only around twenty were not used. Which is just as well: we couldn't afford to shoot *anything* that we were less than sure of.

Which brings me to our co-producer, Helen Watts. Without her fiscal wizardry this film could hardly have been shot at all.

I have also incurred a debt of gratitude to a great many others. These include in Sydney: Joanna Arrowsmith (my toughest critic and strongest supporter); Mal Read (who gave me the idea and a good deal of encouragement); Elizabeth Butcher, Peter Cooke and Jenny Deves at NIDA; Christine Hartgill; my father the late Dr Philip Parsons and my mother Katharine as well as Currency Press and all who sail in her; Justine Saunders; Chris Connors; all those who participated in the first reading of the play including Richard Buckham, Ken Boucher, Harriet Parsons, Peter Hicks, Leo Taylor, Darren Gilshennan, Stewart Robinson, Craig Ilott, Berynn Schwerdt, Carlton Lamb, David James, Murree Bartlett, Deborah Galanos, Jenny Kent. In Alice Springs I am indebted to: Blair McFarland and Meg Mooney (who showed great kindness to a complete stranger), Rob Wenske, Ian McKinlay, Constable Dean Macdonald and Jenny Bartlett. I am indebted to everyone at Kintore, particularly: Peter Holt (who pushed my permit through), Pinta Pinta Tjapananka, Lyle Gamertsfelder, Kerry Arrabena and Nigel Carrick, Linda and Paul, Shane, Ronnie Tjampitjinpa, and, for their instinctive generosity, Bernard Campbell, Matthew West and Adrian Jurra. I am indebted to Paul and Jilau Parker for translating some dialogue and for their generous advice on matters relating to Central Desert people. Thanks also to Dr Bogdan Hulewicz for his advice on forensic matters.

10 August, 1996

MAIN CAST [in order of appearance]

RAY	Bryan Brown
DAVID	Ernie Dingo
KATE	Angie Milliken
TONY	Aaron Pedersen
POPPY	Gnarnayarrahe Waitaire
LES	Lewis Fitz-Gerald
SARAH	Anne Tenney
CHARLIE	John Jarratt
BILLY	Lafe Charlton
TJULPU	Djunawong Stanley Mirindo
MANNGA	Peter Francis

Produced by Bryan Brown and Helen Watts
Written and directed by Nick Parsons
Complete film credits appear at the end of the book.

PRINCIPAL CHARACTERS

SENIOR CONSTABLE RAY LORKIN, white, thirty to forty

POPPY TJUNGURRAYI, elder, Aboriginal, mid-sixties

DAVID MÜLLER, Community Advisor, Aboriginal, mid-thirties

MANNGA TJAPANANGKA, elder, Aboriginal, POPPY's brother in law, mid-sixties

TJULPU TJANGALA, Aboriginal, MANNGA's grandson, early twenties

BILLY CURLEW TJAPALTJARRI, police aide, Aboriginal, mid-twenties

LES MATHIESEN, teacher, white, about forty

KATE MATHIESEN, white, his wife, twenty-nine

TONY McKAY, teaching aide, Aboriginal, mid-twenties

CHARLIE ROTH, anthropologist, white, thirty to forty

SARAH HAMILTON, doctor, white, mid-thirties

GORDON REYNOLDS, television journalist, white, mid-twenties

NIGEL FARRELLY, cameraman, white, mid-twenties

SENIOR SERGEANT WARREN OAKS, white, mid-forties

THE FIRST MAN, Aboriginal, indeterminate age

THE SECOND MAN, Aboriginal, indeterminate age

How this Script Relates to the Screen Version

Curly brackets around text indicate dialogue or scene descriptions that were edited out during the production process.

The '✱' symbol indicates that Scenes 61 & 62 were montaged together to form parts of Scene 63 in the finished film.

Scene 105 from the pre-production script was cut from the film so has no final film version scene number.

SCENE 61   INT. THE KITCHEN – THE DOCTOR'S
RESIDENCE. NIGHT.   {63 ✱}

The penny drops. Sarah shakes her head in mock disbelief.

{SARAH: Some anthropologist.}
CHARLIE: She was having an affair?
SARAH: Of course she was having an affair.

SCENE 62   INT. THE OFFICE – THE POLICE STATION.
NIGHT.   {63 ✱}

The video screen shows Kate with the body. By now Sarah has opened her medical bag and is saying something to Kate. Ray can see himself

. . . .

comes the carcass of a small bird which plops into David's cupped hands. David drops the thing in disgust. Tjulpu laughs raucously. Tjulpu brings up more water and David forces himself to drink. Tjulpu {chews ruminatively on mulbo, a fungus which is acceptable bush food, as he} settles down to work on two pieces of feathered emu skin. What he is making is not too clear. David looks at the tiny corpse, seduced to its death by the fragrance of water. Suddenly Tjulpu cocks his head to listen.

{SCENE 105   INT./ EXT. TOM'S FOUR-WHEEL-DRIVE – THE
SPINIFEX PLAIN. DAY.

The engine roars as Ray urges his vehicle on.}

SCENE 106   EXT. THE SMALL ROCKY OUTCROP – THE
DESERT. DAY.   {107}

David burps and chokes down a wave of nausea as Tjulpu tugs his shoes off and puts them onto his own feet. He has some difficulty with the laces. David watches, bemused.

DAVID: No, no. Ngayuku tjamana nyunnga. Wiya nyuntupa
pirinypa. ['My feet are soft. Not like yours.']

Poppy, an old man dressed in jeans and an ancient coat, sits in the shade of a spindly corkwood tree. He wears a hat but no shoes. He squints into the distance and makes out the approaching figure of an equally shabby first man, who carries two spears and a woomera. From a different angle comes a second man who might be younger than the other two. Poppy stands cheerfully as they draw near and embraces each as he comes up. According to custom the men weep on each other's shoulders for a few moments, then break apart. Poppy produces a pack of cards and the three settle down to play a very basic version of poker.

POPPY: [*pointing west*] You been Jiggalong, eh?

SECOND MAN: Yuwa. [*Spreading out his arms*] I go that one, like an eagle.

> *The wind washes through his hair and for a moment it seems the ground might be passing below.*

One man: I find 'im. Pull out his ribs, take his heart.

> *Distant wailing comes to them across the wind. The First Man listens to the sound with a professional ear.*

FIRST MAN: Ahhh. Finish, eh?

SECOND MAN: [*smiling*] Mmm. That one finish alright.

> *The three men chuckle: all in all it sounds like a good day.*

FIRST MAN: [*pointing north*] I been Balgo. One man: someone sing him, sing out his spirit. I take his arm, suck on it, suck on it. Pretty soon I suck out a blood. Pretty soon I suck out a stone.

SECOND MAN: Ahhh.

FIRST MAN: Someone sing in that stone to kill 'im.

SECOND MAN: Alright now?

FIRST MAN: He been alright. He been good.

> *A general murmur of satisfaction. They throw down their cards.*

SECOND MAN: [*to the First Man*] Eh, look. You win. Big mob of money, eh?

They laugh.

POPPY: I been Wala Wala.

They stop playing. The mood is suddenly sombre.

SECOND MAN: [*quietly*] Finish, that place.
POPPY: Mmm. I finish that one.

> *The Second Man looks at him, impressed. Between the piles of cards Poppy sweeps his hand over the sand to create a blank surface. With four fingers he draws four parallel strokes. An ant crosses towards the strokes. They watch closely as Poppy blows a handful of dust through his fingers across the image. Dissolve to:*

SCENE 2   EXT. THE LOCK-UP – WALA WALA. MORNING.
{2}

The cloud of dust passes to reveal the four strokes have transformed into a bird's-eye view of the bars of the lock-up. The ant has become Billy as he crosses towards it, his body shielding a tray of cornflakes and coffee. Billy wears his neatly ironed police-aide uniform. The lock-up is a besser-brick structure within the police compound, open to the weather and surveillance on one side. As Billy approaches the lock-up he drops the tray and runs.

BILLY: Danny! Eh, wiya, Danny! ['Eh, no, Danny!']

> *He throws open the door and hurls himself inside. After a moment he emerges and sprints across to the policeman's residence.*

Boss! Ray! Ray!

> *Close in on the forbidding mouth of the lock-up.*

SCENE 3   EXT. THE FRONT DOOR – THE POLICE
RESIDENCE. MORNING.   {3}

Ray's house looks like a fortress, with bars on every window. Billy bashes frantically on the security door.

BILLY: Ray!
RAY: [*out of view, muffled*] What? Billy …

There is the sound of bottles being kicked over, then a click from several locks and Ray opens the door half way, groggy with sleep and badly hungover. Only his profile is visible. It is obvious he slept in his uniform.

What? What?

BILLY: You: come. Danny: he been ...

Ray tries to rub some life into his eyes and jumps. For the first time Billy sees he has a black eye, and his lip is badly cut. Billy stares at him, shocked and suddenly unsure.

RAY: What ... Danny? Where – ? Where – ? Why?

SCENE 4   INT. THE LOCK-UP – WALA WALA. MORNING.

{4}

Ray hurtles through the barred door of the lock-up. The sight confronting him brings him up short. He screws up his eyes and shudders: confused and uncertain. Billy watches him warily. The shadow of the hanging man stretches across the concrete floor, next to a slowly growing pool of urine and a single, intricately tooled cowboy boot.

{POPPY: [*voice over, whispering*] Too much ghost.}

A gust of sand blows in. Dissolve to:

SCENE 5   EXT. THE DESERT. DAY.   {5}

Poppy lets the last of the dust fall from his fingers. His simple marks in the sand are now obscured by a smooth layer. The First and Second Man look up, witnesses to all that has transpired. The Second Man sucks his teeth with foreboding.

SECOND MAN: You fix that politpalla, eh?

POPPY: I fix him. Proper one.

Poppy gathers up the cards.

POPPY: Come. I tell you story this one Wala Wala Aboriginal Settlement.

Poppy tosses the cards into the air. They flutter against the sky.

SCENE 6   EXT. WALA WALA. NIGHT.   {6}

Cut to: Sparks fly from the campfire into the raucous night. People shout wildly as the temperature of the mob rises in anticipation of a traditional payback spearing. At the centre of the melee two desert Aborigines – the old man Mannga and his grandson Tjulpu, the former armed with a heavy payback spear – threaten Tony, a young man much like Tjulpu but slightly older and more urban in dress and manner. Poppy and the First and Second Man observe from the sidelines.

MANNGA: Ngayuku minali mirrirrngu!* ['My boy is dead!']

Heedless of the spear, Tony advances furiously on Mannga.

TONY: I never got 'im drink; he just sit down with us!

The First and Second Man look at Poppy with alarm, but Poppy follows the action.

MANNGA: Ngayuku minali mirrirrngu! ['My boy is dead!']
DAVID: Hey, hey! Tony's got nothing to do!

David, also Aboriginal, pushes himself between them. He is community adviser and local pastor, burdened with responsibility and care.

{DAVID: This is no good: you finish, eh?}

He attempts to restrain Tony, who easily pulls away.

TONY: He got his own drink, I don't give it to him.

With a sudden flash of anger, Tjulpu lunges at Tony. The two scuffle in the dirt.

He ... was a ... fuckin' piss pot!
DAVID: Finish! Enough! {This is no good!}

David collects an elbow in the face before he drags Tony off and down in the dust. The mob yells indiscriminately. Poppy leaves the side of the First and Second Man. He hisses into Mannga's ear.

---

* Subtitle required on screen.

POPPY: [*indicating Tony*] Palangku Tonylu ngalyakatingu tjurratja yungu nyuntupa katiaku. ['That one brought drink to your son.'] He drink, politpalla put 'im lock-up.

> *Tony pushes David out of the way and struggles to his feet. He turns on Poppy and the two men argue ferociously, head to head. Mannga orders Tjulpu back and he obeys instantly.*

TONY: [*indicating Mannga*] Palaru nyuntupa marutju! ['That one's your brother in law!'] You're uncle to that lock-up one. You don't look after that one. You did it wrong way!

POPPY: No! You get 'im drink: you do it wrong way!

TONY: [*to Mannga, pointing an accusing finger at Poppy*] He didn't look after him! Wrong way!

> *Mannga now covers both Tony and Poppy with the spear. Suddenly, lights blazing, the police vehicle hoves into view. There is a blip from the siren and Ray and Billy emerge. Ray carries his gun belt, which he straps on as he approaches.*

RAY: [*to all*] Alright, shut up! Shut up the lot of you! Shut up!

> *Relative silence. Ray looks around: all eyes are on him.*

[*to Mannga, indicating the spear*] You: what your name?

> *Mannga glares at him.*

BENSON: That one Mannga. He father that lock-up one.

RAY: He's ... what?

BENSON: That lock-up one: his little fella.

> *Ray is stunned. He glances at Billy: did he know about this? Billy looks away nervously.*

POPPY: Payback one. You watpalla go.

RAY: No.

MANNGA: Aboriginal law. You go.

RAY: No. No chance. [*Indicating himself*] Watpalla law. I stay. [*To all*] What is all this? This Wala Wala way? You want to kill someone? Eh?

> *An uneasy pause.*

{RAY: [*To Mannga*] We're all sorry for your son. Everyone. We're all sorry. But in Wala Wala, you want payback, we do it proper one. We make a time and a place. We choose one fella. [*Holding up one finger*] One only. Okay? [*Indicating his thigh*] You pay him back here, then finish. Okay? Fair enough?} Otherwise you go lock-up. Maybe lock-up Alice Springs. Alright?

(Note: in the filmed scene the line above replaces bracketed dialogue below.) Mannga glares at him.

MANNGA: You watpalla go.

Pause. Mannga hefts his spear slightly. Ray picks up the motion.

RAY: Alright. You want payback? Eh? Your son? You want payback?

MANNGA: Yuwa.

David wilts: he knows what's coming.

RAY: Okay. You choose one. One fella now, then all finish. Okay? {One fella now; that's it. Otherwise lock-up.}

Mannga stares at him, then grudgingly looks around at the crowd for a victim.

TONY: [*nervously*] Ray ...

RAY: Shut up.

Mannga looks Tony up and down, then continues to search through the crowd. Some uneasy shuffling. Poppy observes Mannga's scrutiny coming his way. Now he's desperate and angry.

POPPY: [*to Mannga, indicating Ray*] That one put him lock-up. Politpalla!

DAVID: Hey!

POPPY: [*to Ray, indicating Mannga*] That boy, you take 'im, put 'im lock-up, he finish!

RAY: You said your piece, have you? Maybe you want to go lock-up too?

DAVID: Hey, Ray, come on ...

Poppy looks at Ray angrily, but says nothing. Mannga slowly approaches Ray and looks him in the eyes. Ray doesn't move. The tip of the spear brushes Ray's thigh.

[*cautiously*] Ray ...

Ray silences him with a gesture. Suddenly Mannga raises the spear and points it at Billy.

MANNGA: That one.

A murmur of approval goes around the crowd. It is a canny choice.

RAY: No.

MANNGA: That one.

RAY: I said, 'No'. Not police.

MANNGA: [*interrupting, pointing at Ray*] You give me one. [*Pointing the spear at Billy*] I take t hat one.

RAY: I said, 'No', fuck you.

Mannga takes a step back and raises his spear at Ray.

[*drawing his pistol*] Oh, yeah? Yeah?

Poppy grabs Mannga's wrist as Billy jumps between them.

BILLY: Boss! It okay.

RAY: Get out of the way.

BILLY: You settle down.

RAY: [*to Billy*] No, fuck off. Get the fuckin' cuffs out and put 'em on that bastard.

BILLY: It okay. I do it wrong way.

RAY: No, you didn't. He bloody-well ... He bloody hung himself! You had ... nothing to do.

BILLY: Aboriginal law, Ray. That one been lock-up, I don't look after him. Gotta make it even; do proper-one payback. Like you say.

Billy goes to Mannga. The shouting dies down again. David appeals silently to Ray, who looks away.

BILLY: Eh, Tjapananka.

Mannga looks at Billy a moment, then nods. Billy takes his trousers off, folds them neatly and hands them to Ray. Ray looks at Billy.

Don't worry, Boss. I can make that pain not hurt.

Ray clutches the trousers as Billy goes to Mannga. The shouting starts up again. A circle forms around them, separating Billy from Ray. Billy presents his thigh. Ray observes Mannga drive the spear into Billy's leg, then lean on it with all his weight. The spear goes straight through. Mannga withdraws it and drives the spear in once more. Tony looks on. The First and Second Man watch Ray's reaction as Mannga grinds the shaft around once or twice, then withdraws it. Billy wavers for a moment. Mannga prepares for a third strike, but Billy passes out. Mannga steps back, satisfied. The two women with nulla nullas rush forward and begin to pound Billy about the head. Ray can stand it no longer. He drags the women off.

RAY: That's it! Enough! Finish! All finish! Leave him!

The crowd separates, the shouting dies. Ray kneels by Billy's prone form and touches his leg. He draws his hand away covered in blood.

DAVID: I'll ... I'll get Sarah.

David leaves. Ray stares at Mannga.

RAY: I hope you're satisfied.

Mannga holds his gaze, turns and slowly and leaves. Poppy looks down at the bleeding man, then at Ray. He too turns and saunters off. The First and Second Man join him.

SCENE 7   INT./EXT. THE CLASSROOM – THE SCHOOL. DAY.   {7}

On the board are two sentences: 'The door was broken. The axle was broke.' The schoolteacher, Les Mathiesen, has used a different colour for the 'n' in 'broken', which is his correction. He writes another 'n' on the end of the last sentence.

LES: 'The axle was broken.' Is *this* a sentence?

> *The class shouts 'Yeah'. Les consults the exercise book in his hand. The third sentence reads, in childish scrawl, 'The car been fucked'. Les looks at Justin, the young Aboriginal author, who glances mischievously at his friend Sonia, who smiles back. Sonia and her brother Adrian are the only two white children in class. Les turns back to the board.*

SCENE 8   INT./EXT. THE OFFICE – THE SCHOOL. DAY. {8}

Kate Mathiesen, an attractive white woman of twenty-nine, slogs though a pile of government forms using an old electric typewriter. Through the window she notices an Aboriginal man and woman laugh as they pass by. Suddenly Tony's face appears at the window; he is spattered with white paint. Tony holds up the paint roller he's been using on the outer wall of the office, then blows her a kiss. Tony is a charmer of almost irresistible proportions. To cover her confusion, Kate looks down and continues to type.

JUSTIN: [*out of view*] Eh! Tony! You keep painting you be watpalla pretty soon.

SCENE 9   EXT. THE SCHOOL – WALA WALA. DAY.   {9}

Tony turns to see Justin crawling through a broken panel in the wall of the classroom. He gives the boy a broad bespattered smile.

TONY: You be ignorant blackfella all your bloody life, you don't get in that classroom.

> *Behind the smiling boy Tony becomes aware of a couple of trucks with people disembarking. One or two carry spears and seem to be painted up. An Aboriginal man in white ochre glances at Tony, spattered with white paint. Tony looks back uneasily. The man turns off to the classroom.*

SCENE 10   INT./ EXT. THE CLASSROOM – THE SCHOOL.
DAY.   {10}

*On the board Les has written, 'The car' and in a different colour, 'was
damaged beyond repair'. The Aboriginal man, face painted in white
clay for the ceremony, leans in the window.*

ABORIGINAL MAN: Eh ... No school. Finish.
LES: [*nonplussed*] Well ... Why?
ABORIGINAL MAN: Sorry business.

> *Behind the man Les sees people clamber out of vehicles. Many are
> painted up for a ceremony in white, black and brown and carry
> spears.*

{SCENE 11   INT./ EXT. THE CONSULTING ROOM – THE
CLINIC. DAY.

*The settlement appears empty but the wailing of women and dogs
carries in the oppressive air. Ray stares restlessly through the window,
smoking. Billy lies on a stretcher, eyes closed, his lower half covered by
a sheet with a widening bloodstain. Sarah leafs through an ancient
edition of* Time *without much interest.*

RAY: Christ, I could do with a beer.

> *Sarah picks up her cold coffee, grimaces and puts it down again.*

SARAH: Isn't there some at the station?
RAY: Yeah ...
SARAH: Well ... I could ... sneak out.
RAY: Yeah ... No, better not. No point getting us both in the shit.

> *Sarah lets out a long breath. She joins Ray by the window, takes
> the cigarette from his fingers and draws back on it.*

RAY: Thought you didn't smoke.
SARAH: [*handing it back*] I don't. I'm not.

> *She goes to Billy and pulls down the sheet. His bandages are
> caked in blood. She begins to change them.*

SARAH: Any word from Alice ... about Danny's inquest?
RAY: No. It'll be fine.

> *Ray watches her strip the bloody bandage off. He feels responsible.*

I did stop a payback once. As a young fella.
SARAH: Oh, yeah?
RAY: It all blew up again next day, though. In the ceremony. All the relatives about; it was ... pretty ugly.

> *Sarah stares at him.*

You can't interfere, you know? They're not gunna wait for an inquest. They want justice where they can see it.
SARAH: Obviously.

> *Sarah goes back to the bandages. Ray turns to the window.*

RAY: They like to get things squared up before a funeral.
SARAH: I wonder how Charlie's going.}

SCENE 12   EXT. CEREMONIAL GROUND – NEAR WALA WALA. DAY.   {11}

Charlie Roth lies face down in the dirt with the women and the children. Around him white ochred feet pound the dirt to the singing and wailing of the mourners. Concealed in his hand is the blinking red light of a tiny microcassette recorder. As the dancing continues he takes a surreptitious peek at the proceedings and has dirt kicked in his face. Probably an accident.

SCENE 13   INT./EXT. THE LIVING ROOM – THE TEACHER'S RESIDENCE. DAY.   {12}

Les holds back the cloth on a small half-finished landscape in oils. Kate swigs from a bottle of mineral water. They too have cabin fever.

LES: I only said it's good!
KATE: [*covering the painting*] It's not anything. Just therapy, for God sake.
LES: Alright.

Kate splashes mineral water on her face. Les watches this waste with annoyance. Tony enters from the back room, still in his paint-spattered clothes.

TONY: Well ... Ray Martin's over.

KATE: Is the movie on?

TONY: Yeah, piece of shit. Some Yank fella in sandals with a big sword. I watched a bit of it.

LES: Shouldn't you be at the sorry business?

TONY: Aaah ... Danny's funeral: not my business. Anyhow, they'll be at it for years yet.

He exchanges a mischievous glance with Kate.

LES: Ah.

Les stares out the window. With Les' back turned, Tony moves over to Kate until he's standing uncomfortably close. Les is entranced by the landscape: ochre and olive green beneath a startling blue sky. It's spectacular.

So harsh a place, but God, I love this country.

Tony joins Les by the window. He scans the scene.

TONY: Why?

Somewhere an electric guitar is played, very badly at fearsome volume.

LES: Must be over.

KATE: He never gets any better, does he?

TONY: Petrol sniffer. Sound deadly to him.

The painful guitar bridges into:

SCENE 14   INT./ EXT. THE CONSULTING ROOM – THE CLINIC. DAY.   {13}

Charlie enters the clinic with Ray's coat bundled under his arm. Ray and Sarah gather eagerly as he unrolls it and takes out four cans of VB. (Note: for production purposes all VBs became Fosters.)

SARAH: You're an angel.
CHARLIE: Contraband.

> *As Sarah reaches for her can Charlie puts a dusty arm around her and kisses her on the cheek. Ray observes her as she playfully pushes him away. Ray reaches for a can and returns to the window.*

RAY: Thanks, mate.
CHARLIE: Pray the cops don't spring us.

> *Ray gives him a narky grin. Outside he sees a lone figure with a coat over his head weave down the road. Mannga, Tjulpu and Poppy appear. With an angry gesture Poppy breaks away from the others and pulls the coat off the young man's head: the young man has the lip of a can between his teeth. Poppy lectures him angrily and tries to grab the can, but the young man slaps him away. Poppy is mortified at this behaviour in front of the newcomers.*

BILLY: [*groggily*] Mmm. Beer.
RAY: Oh, you're awake now?
SARAH: No, no. Not for you, sport.

> *Ray and Sarah grin at each other. Over the following Ray observes the young man yank his coat away from Poppy, look at the old man indifferently for a few seconds, then weave off. Poppy shouts after him, then gives up. Mannga and Tjulpu stare at the ground.*

CHARLIE: Hey, palya, Billy? ['Are you well, Billy?']
BILLY: Yuwa.
CHARLIE: Good on you.
SARAH: How was the ceremony?
CHARLIE: [*shrugging*] Ohhh ...

> *He avoids the question. Poppy meets Ray's eyes as Ray takes a swig of his beer. Poppy realises with bitterness that Ray has witnessed his embarrassment. Ray turns back into the room.*

RAY: Steer clear of all that myself. Don't even want a skin name.
I'd have to collar my own relatives.

A light plane passes overhead. All three react at once.

SARAH: [*handing Ray her can*] I'll bring the car round.
CHARLIE: I'll come with you.

> *Charlie puts an arm around her as they leave. Ray stares at Billy for a moment, a beer in each hand. Pause.*

RAY: We'll put you on a plane now. Take you Alice Springs.
BILLY: [*groggily*] Mmm.
RAY: Have a holiday, you brave bastard.
BILLY: Good one.

> *Billy nods.*

RAY: You know there's a ... in Alice, an inquiry. Into what happened with Danny. {Police inquiry.} You know what that is?
BILLY: Coroner.
RAY: Yeah. Like the coroner, yeah. But a ... police one. Internal police {one}. I've gotta prove I did everything I could to ... to prevent what happened. {Prevent how he ... how he hung himself.} What d'you think? You think I did everything I could?

> *Billy is silent.*

Yeah, I liked him; I thought he was a good bloke. I thought it was a shame he died.

> *He swigs one of the beers.*

You think I drink too much?

> *Silence.*

Billy?
BILLY: No.
RAY: No, me neither. No, stone cold sober most days. Not like Danny, eh?

> *Billy is silent. Ray hardens his tone slightly.*

I said, 'Not like Danny, eh?'

Billy shakes his head.

RAY: No. His state was far from sober.
BILLY: That one been violent and abusive.
RAY: That's right.
BILLY: [*miming a punch in the eye*] He punch you that one.
RAY: Yeah, he did. Yeah. But I didn't crack. I was stone sober. Eh?
BILLY: Yuwa.

> *Ray {runs a hand through Billy's hair, then} puts a can of beer in his hands.*

RAY: Yeah, Billy Boy. Have a go at that one.

SCENE 15   EXT. WALA WALA. DAY.   {15}

Sunday morning. The settlement is dotted with people heading for church. Poppy regards them from his regal position in the front seat of his derelict Toyota. All the glass in the vehicle has been smashed and several panels have bullet holes in them. David passes him in full vestments and waves cheerily. It is like a casual meeting of church an d state.

DAVID: Eh, number-one singer: you coming?
POPPY: Eh! You: give me Toyota.

> *Poppy jumps down and they walk together.*

DAVID: Eh, no Poppy.
POPPY: You write letter. Government.

> {*David spots Mannga and Tjulpu sitting in the shade of one of the houses. Mannga watches all this Christian activity with hostility. David finds his gaze vaguely disturbing; Poppy is unaffected.*}

DAVID: No, no. [*Turning to Poppy, indicating the derelict Toyota*] You smash up that one.
POPPY: [*outraged*] No!

> *David takes an ironic look at the state of the vehicle, {then continues on. Mannga watches them go.}*

DAVID: I get you one next year.

POPPY: That Toyota mine!

DAVID: Yeah, true. And Tjungurrayi, you got a rifle and you shot it to bits.

POPPY: Yuwa.

DAVID: [*turning to the vehicle*] And you smash all the windows.

POPPY: [*regarding the tragic remains*] Yuwa. Big fight.

DAVID: That's no good. Big mob of money, that Toyota.

{*They continue towards the church.*}

POPPY: Yuwa. You get me 'nudder one.

DAVID: I can't.

POPPY: Government.

DAVID: No, Government's got nothing to do. Maybe next year. [*Stopping*] You got a big fine for shooting up that Toyota. Ray sent you Alice Springs; remember? I can't get you another one yet.

Poppy stares at him, then looks over at the police compound.

POPPY: Fucking bastard.

DAVID: Hey, Poppy!

It is Sunday, after all. Poppy looks a little sheepish. People are gathered outside the church – basically an old tin shed with a dirt floor – in their Sunday best. Poppy gestures towards the dark hole of the lock-up.

POPPY: He finish that lock-up one.

DAVID: No, no, no. That's watpalla business now. Mannga's got payback for that one. All finish.

Poppy {puts a hand on David's shoulder and} leans close.

POPPY: [*softly*] Someone fix that politpalla. Proper one.

Poppy looks at him steadily. David suddenly catches sight of Les leading Adrian and Sonia. David smiles cheerily.

DAVID: Les. Kate not here today?

LES: [*smiling uncertainly*] No. No, not today.

Les hurries on. It's a sore point.

SCENE 16   EXT. KUNINKA WATERHOLE. DAY.   {16}

Unlike Wala Wala the waterhole is very beautiful. Tony lies in the shade of a tree; he wears dark glasses and no shirt. Nearby is the esky. He looks up at Kate, who stands with her easel on a rock ledge.

TONY: You getting red. You want some cream?
KATE: Oh ... Thanks.

> *Tony goes to the esky and finds a tube of block-out cream. He scales the rock in a couple of leaps. Kate holds out her hand for the tube, but Tony squirts cream on her wrist instead. He smooths it into her arm.*

TONY: How old are you?
KATE: Why?

> *Tony shrugs.*

I'm twenty-nine. How old are you?
TONY: How old is Les?
KATE: He's forty.
TONY: Uh. That's blackfella way: get 'em young. I got a girl promised me. She be fourteen soon.

> *Tony works his way up to her shoulder.*

KATE: Um ... Les ... Les ...
TONY: Yeah?
KATE: Les thought you might give that new boy some English lessons.
TONY: Tjulpu?
KATE: Yes, he's – he's – he's very much behind.
TONY: No ...
KATE: You'd get a ... a tutor's fee.
TONY: I teach that boy English, [*prodding her thigh*] I think that old man spear me this one.

> *He kneels and begins to anoint her legs.*

KATE: Why?
TONY: Tjulpu: he's Danny's little kid. Watpallas took him off

Danny, put 'im orphanage. That old man Mannga: he stole that boy away, [*pointing*] took him out that way, years ago. They live in desert ever since. Tjulpu: he's just about never seen a watpalla, never been to school. He's real blackfella.

KATE: That's ... an awful story.

TONY: Yeah. Back then Government take kids all time. I grew up orphanage.

KATE: Oh. I'm sorry.

TONY: Yeah, no good. They gave me new name, everything ... Wish someone come and stole me back, eh? But no one did.

Kate looks down at him and touches his head lightly.

KATE: You're ... You're very bright, Tony. You could do anything, you know.

TONY: Yeah? I be boss of Les one day, you reckon?

Kate doesn't know how to take this. At last Tony points.

My country's that way, my Dreaming.

KATE: But you don't believe in that. You – You told me.

TONY: Yeah, true. But ... I get lonely for my country. You stop believing one way, you don't start believing another.

Kate looks at him uncertainly. Suddenly Tony smiles.

I believe you gotta have a bit of fun, but, eh?

His hands slide further up her legs. Kate pulls away.

KATE: Tony ...

Tony touches her face, then starts to undo her dress. Kate tries to break away but he holds her firmly. She lets him take her dress off. He rubs cream over the rest of her body.

I burn so easily.

TONY: That's nature saying, 'Go home, white man'. [*Indicating the tube*] This watpalla way to say nature can get stuffed.

Kate laughs.

KATE: Tony: this ... I'm – I mean it, you know. This must be the last time.

Tony takes some of the fine sand and pours it over her.

This is not what I ... what I ... Oh. What are you doing?
TONY: [*grinning*] Oh ... keep you safe {from pankalangu.
KATE: What's that?
TONY: Spirit. He lives round waterhole like this one. We trick 'im:
he don't see you're white woman.

Tony is gradually turning her completely ochre.

KATE: No. I suppose not.
TONY: You come along this way.}

*He {grins, then} moves over to the crevice in the cliff face. He
looks at her. {She hesitates.*

Eh. Look out for pankalangu.}

He disappears inside.

{KATE: Tony ... [*To herself*] 'Pankalangu' ...}

She looks about at the high cliff walls. A silence has fallen.

KATE: Tony? ... Tony?

No answer. Gradually she inches her way into the crevice.

SCENE 17   EXT. MEN'S BUSINESS CLEARING. DAY.   {17}

*Music: a mixture of choral harmonies and Aboriginal rhythm. The
ground is covered with an elaborate sand painting incorporating
feathers, shells, heavily designed shields. She stares in silence, aware that
she is engaged in something outside her experience. {Tony's dark arms
snake around her from behind. One hand slides into her pants – her last
item of clothing and last line of defence. His other hand moves down and
she feels the fabric torn away.} Tony's mouth whispers close to her ear.*

TONY: This is where we kill boys ... and make men.

SCENE 18   INT. THE CHURCH – WALA WALA. DAY.   {18}

*Les, Sonia and Adrian belt out a hymn with their Aboriginal brethren.
(Note: in the filmed scene they sing 'The Lord is My Shepherd'.) There is*

no altar or organ because the termites ate them. A few mangy dogs wander among the legs of the faithful.

SCENE 19   INT./EXT. MONTAGE. DAY.   {19}

The music bridges over Tony and Kate making love among the sacred objects. A dogfight starts in the church; the snapping jaws blend with the thrashing bodies of the lovers in the dust. {Kate's hand, spotted in oil paint, grasps the rock wall.} The snarling dogs for a moment threaten to overwhelm the singing until a couple of bystanders stop the fight with a few swift kicks. The dogs yelp and fall apart.

SCENE 20   INT. THE MUSTER ROOM – THE POLICE STATION. DAY.   {20}

A new day. Tjulpu's smiling face looks out of the front page of the Centralian Advocate. *Above the photo is a byline: 'Last of the nomads'.*

RAY: Look: you can't take pictures of a sacred site. People really get the shits.
GORDON: We didn't!
RAY: How do you know?

> *The reporter, Gordon Reynolds, grinds to a halt. He and his cameraman, Nigel Farrelly, stand uncomfortably in the middle of the muster room as Ray tilts a chair back with a deceptively casual air. The newcomers have been driving since dawn: they're sweaty, wrinkled and tired. Farrelly's Betacam sits on the desk. David leans against the wall at a slight distance, holding the paper.*

DAVID: [*waving the paper*] Where'd this come from? The photo.
GORDON: Um ... guy who worked here. Driving instructor.

> *Ray and David glance at one another in exasperation.*

RAY: You got a permit?
GORDON: Yeah, *absolutely.* I mean ... well, no. We – We – We could apply for one now, though, couldn't we?
RAY: [*indicating David*] You better ask him: that's his job.
GORDON: [*to David*] Sorry; you work here, do you?

SCENE 21   INT. THE OFFICE – THE SCHOOL. DAY.   {21}

Spectacular red cliffs: an image in a picture book. Les watches Tjulpu leaf through the book at great speed, with scant regard for how many pages he tears. Each image shows another aspect of the Australian centre.

TJULPU: Ngaanya. ['This one.']
LES: Um ... 'MacDonnell Ranges'.
TJULPU: [*pointing into the distance*] Ngarrawana. ['That way.']
LES: That's right.
TJULPU: [*turning the page*] Mmm. Ngaanya. ['This one.']
LES: Ummm ... Oh. 'Bungle Bungles, W.A.'
TJULPU: [*pointing in the opposite direction*] Ngarrawana. ['That way.']
LES: [*now somewhat confused*] Aaah ... yes.
TJULPU: [*observing his confusion*] Tjingaru ngarrawana. ['Maybe that way.']

> *Tjulpu turns the page and comes across a macro shot of the head of a bull ant. He jumps up in horror.*

Whoah!

> *Les laughs and Tjulpu joins in. Their laughter is interrupted by the presence of Mannga at the door. Les notices a hatchet dangling from one hand. Pause.*

LES: [*to Mannga*] Can I help you?

SCENE 22   INT. THE MUSTER ROOM – THE POLICE
STATION. DAY.   {22}

Gordon stares at Ray in disbelief. Farrelly, insecure without his camera, stares out the window.

GORDON: 'Two to four *weeks*'?

> *Farrelly's eyebrows head for the ceiling as he observes Les sprinting towards the station, Mannga in close pursuit, shouting and waving his hatchet in the air. A straggling crowd runs after them, shouting.*

DAVID: I'd go back to Alice if I were you.

GORDON: But ... that's an eight-hour drive.

Gordon looks from one to the other. Ray is unmoved. Farrelly, engrossed in the drama outside, sees Poppy negotiating with his brother-in-law, eventually succeeding in making him stop and listen. Farrelly looks at his camera longingly. Gordon takes the paper from David and gestures at the photo.

Look: the old man, his grandson, first contact and all that: it's a good story. You know? And I mean, let's face it, there's gunna be a shitload of press turning up to talk to 'em. *Or* you could deal with us. Right now. Let the story die a natural death. We're just out here try'n'a get a bit of depth. It'll take us maybe half a day.

DAVID: [*indicating the paper*] Well ... the story isn't quite true, you know.

Les bursts into the station.

LES: Oh ... Ray, thank God. I've just been chased around the school by a – a – a *madman* wielding a *hatchet* like a ...

He is interrupted as Poppy charges in.

POPPY: Eh! You: that one no English!

LES: Oh, I think English, yes!

Gordon looks at his partner, alarmed. Farrelly looks back placidly.

POPPY: No! Tjulpu no English. [*Miming a spear*] Mannga fix you proper one!

LES: He must go to school. That's whitefella law.

POPPY: No! We teach that one. We do it right way!

RAY: [*shouting*] What the bloody hell is going on here?

Silence. Poppy looks at Ray with open hostility.

DAVID: Les ... Poppy ... This is ... Gordon and Nigel. They're ... reporters.

GORDON: [*to Les, with a smile, offering a hand*] Seven Network. Hi.

LES: [*stunned*] Hello.

FARRELLY: [*also shaking hands*] Yep.
POPPY: [*indicating Gordon*] Ahhh, television.
GORDON: [*offering a hand*] Ah ... yeah. Nice to meet you.
POPPY: You: give me money.

Gordon is nonplussed. Ray groans inwardly.

SCENE 23   EXT. THE TEACHER'S RESIDENCE – WALA
WALA. DAY.   {23}

Kate keeps a protective hand on each of her children as they approach their house. Looking up, she notices a broken window next to the front door. She quickens their pace. (Note: in the finished film an unscripted scene was introduced here which reveals Kate is being observed through binoculars by a child sitting in Gordon and Farrelly's four-wheel-drive.)

SCENE 24   INT./EXT. THE MUSTER ROOM – THE POLICE
STATION. DAY.   {25}

Ray watches through the window as Gordon and Farrelly, minus camera, head back to their rented four-wheel-drive. A child jumps out of the vehicle. (Note: in the finished film there are two children.) Farrelly yells and breaks into a run as he realises the kid is carrying his binoculars. Ray watches ironically but does nothing: he can sense they mean trouble. David and Les both look expectantly at Poppy, who remains seated with a look of consternation on his face.

LES: He *needs* English lessons.
RAY: Oh, for G od sake.
LES: Well, Ray: in that case, what are we doing here? I mean, I can't even teach *English*, exactly what are we supposed to be doing here?
DAVID: Alright, that's enough. Les: I don't think we can insist Tjulpu goes to school. But I think Mannga should go and I think Tjulpu should go with him. At least for a while. That's tribal way.
LES: In that case I'd rather drop the whole thing.
POPPY: [*to David*] No. Mannga stay.

RAY: Then I take 'im Alice Springs, I put 'im lock-up, eh? You like that one?

POPPY: No, that one stay! Tjulpu stay! You go! You go, fucking bastard. You go, [*to Les*] you go ...

He turns to include David, then hesitates. He turns back to Ray.

Mannga stay.

RAY: I'll give you till Wednesday. If he's here Wednesday I take 'im Alice Springs.

Poppy stalks out. David groans inwardly.

DAVID: You know where he's gone now, don't you? Talk to those reporters.

RAY: Ah, who gives a shit?

DAVID: Ray ... you're not solving the problem.

LES: I'm sorry. I don't see this has anything to do with me at all. I've said I'd rather drop the whole thing and I certainly don't want that young boy sent out in the desert again just because of his grandfather.

RAY: Oh, get fucked.

LES: [*to David*] I think that's the end of the meeting. I'll speak with you later.

Les leaves. Anger wells up in David.

DAVID: Ray, I ... am trying ... to balance the needs —

RAY: [*interrupting*] You're such a fucking bureaucrat, you know that?

DAVID: Yes.

RAY: It's obvious they have to go, Dave: the place is a fucking mess. Someone like Tjulpu: he's a nice kid, but he'll get on the grog, he'll start sniffing, he'll just ... lose himself. Few years down the track he'll spend a night in the lock-up and we'll find 'im ... hung up like someone's overcoat.

They stare at one another.

RAY: Ah, fuck. I'm sorry, mate. I'm just ... This place is fucked. You know that, don't you? Sooner or later it's just gunna ...

DAVID: Ray, the Council wants me to write a letter requesting you be transferred.

RAY: Oh. Right.

> *Pause.*

The Council, eh? You gunna write that letter?
DAVID: Have to.
RAY: Fuck it. Fuck. This is over Poppy's bloody Toyota, you know.
DAVID: No, it's not.
RAY: Of course it bloody is. {At bottom. He shoots the fuckin' thing to pieces, and I'm the big villain because I sent 'im down for it.} It was only a fuckin' fine, you know; it's not like he spent his ... you know, his life in prison. Now he's out to get me.

> *They stare at one another.*

I got you this job in the first place.
DAVID: I know that, Ray.
RAY: If it wasn't for me you'd still be running round the country spreading God's word for the Lutheran Fucking Church.
DAVID: I *know*, alright?
RAY: But you'll shaft me all the same.
{DAVID: Why do you think I'm warning you? Listen: it'll blow over ... if you play your cards right.}

SCENE 25   INT. THE LIVING ROOM – THE TEACHER'S RESIDENCE. DAY.   {26}

Kate's painting is gone. She stares hopelessly at her empty easel. In one hand is the cloth normally used to cover it.

ADRIAN: [*out of view*] Mum! They got my Ferrari Testarossa!

> *The house is in chaos: open cupboards, clothes and books strewn about the floor. In the kitchen the fridge is empty. Kate feels her daughter's hand curl around her own.*

SONIA: Don't worry, Mum.

> *Kate can only stare hopelessly at the empty easel, struck by a secret fear.*

SCENE 26 INT./EXT. TONY'S TRUCK – THE DESERT.
NIGHT.   {27}

Tony drives through the night, Country and Western blasting through clapped-out speakers. Suddenly the lights pick up Ray's Toyota parked on the embankment. Tony looks in alarm at his rear-view mirror: sure enough the lights come on, the vehicle pulls out and closes on him.

TONY: Ah, shit. Ah, fuck. Ah, fuck it. {Fuck. Fuck.}

> *The siren blips and lights flash.*

Ah, fuck!

> *Tony pulls over to the side and the Toyota parks behind him. A door slams and Ray strolls over, shotgun dangling casually from one hand.*

Eh, Ray.
RAY: Tony. G'day.

> *He leans on the window and looks around inside the cabin.*

Cold night. Long trip?
TONY: Papunya.
RAY: Oh, yeah.

> *Tony stares at him. Ray leaves the window and strolls around the back.*

TONY: Uh ... What you come out here for?
RAY: Oh ... just noticed you weren't about. Thought I'd drive out, see if I ran into you. Thought you might've been to Alice Springs.
TONY: No.
RAY: You got a bit of a load on the back.

> *Tony says nothing. Ray appears at the passenger window. The courtesy light comes on as he opens the door and sits in the seat.*

Got your licence handy?

> *Tony produces his licence. Ray glances at it without real interest.*

And the keys, thanks.

> *Tony hesitates, then pulls the keys from the ignition. He fumbles and drops them. Ray stares at him.*

You nervous, Tony?

> *Tony scrabbles on the floor but can't find them in the dark. He opens the driver's door so he can kneel in the dirt. Ray gets out.*

SCENE 27   EXT. TONY'S TRUCK – THE DESERT. NIGHT.{28}

Tony stands up and dangles the keys victoriously. He tosses them across the roof and Ray snatches them out of the air as he moves around the back of the vehicle. A tarpaulin covers a bulky load, securely tied down.

RAY: Mind if I take a look?

> *Tony runs around the other side.*

TONY: Ray, come on ...

> *Ray looks at him.*

You're my friend, eh?
RAY: I'm everybody's friend.
TONY: I'm your friend.
RAY: How d'y ou mean?
TONY: {Maybe ... someone try'n'a make you go.} I could be your friend. {Maybe tell you ... what people saying.} Maybe talk up for you at meeting. Talk up for you with the ... with the whitefellas, at inquest. You gotta have plenty friend, Ray. You need someone who look out for you.

> *Ray looks at him.*

RAY: Maybe you're right.

> *Ray turns and walks behind the vehicle. Tony grins.*

TONY: Yeah, I'm right. I be your friend, don't you worry. You be okay.

> *Ray points the shotgun at the tray.*

Ray?

Tony dives for cover as Ray lets off several blasts into the tarpaulin. With each blast comes a foamy explosion and smashed glass. A mixture of beer and wine flows onto the sand. The job is done in a few seconds. Ray wanders over to Tony, who lies shocked and prone on the dirt. Ray drops the licence next to him and starts back to his own vehicle.

Ray, you fuckin' arsehole.
{RAY: Yeah?}
TONY: [*rising*] You don't stop me before.

Ray points the gun at him. Tony freezes.

RAY: I'm stopping you now.

Tony doesn't move.

You have a few drinks out bush with Andrew and Benson, that's one thing. I didn't say you could bring it in town.
TONY: I don't bring it in town. We go out bush with that.
RAY: You wanna tell me where Danny got his last drink from? You wanna tell me that?
TONY: You drink plenty.
RAY: [*pointing the gun at him*] What?

Tony shrugs. Ray jams the shotgun in his face.

Don't bring any more grog back here. Alright?

Ray goes back to his vehicle.

TONY: Eh, gimme keys.

Ray takes the keys from his pocket and tosses them into the darkness.

TONY: Hey! I gotta drive home.
RAY: If you're a real Abo you'll walk.

Ray gets into his car, starts it up and drives away. Tony waits a few judicious seconds before screaming his head off.

TONY: You fuckin' arsehole! You can't tell us what to do. Eh, watpalla, you hear? You can't tell us nothing!

The tail lights finally become a red haze on the horizon and disappear. Tony looks in despair at the ruins of his enterprise, then goes back to the cabin and sits in the driver's seat. He reaches down near the pedals and picks up the car keys from where he dropped them.

Real Abo don't give his car keys to no politpalla.

SCENE 28   EXT. POPPY'S HOUSE – WALA WALA. NIGHT.{29}

Mannga gestures to an Aboriginal Boy to approach: {the same youngster Tony admonished the day after the payback. The boy is now dressed in a pretty pink jumper which we have seen Sonia wearing.} He hands Mannga an object wrapped in an old blanket. Mannga dismisses him with a gesture, then carefully removes Kate's painting. He and Poppy are seated by a campfire. In the background a woman glances at them. Mannga looks at her angrily. She hurriedly shields her eyes and goes into the house. Mannga turns back to Poppy and passes him the painting. Poppy stares at it.

MANNGA: Teacher woman ... make this one.

{Clearly depicted is the crevice in the rock through which Tony lured Kate.} Poppy stares at Mannga, filled with horror and a deep sense of panic. {He begins to rock from side to side.} Mannga takes the painting and tosses it onto the fire. {Poppy takes handfuls of sand and throws them hopelessly over his head.} The First and Second Man seem to have magically appeared from the darkness. The Second Man sucks his teeth with apprehension. Poppy and the First and Second Man stare as, one by one, the features in the painting are consumed.

SCENE 29   EXT. THE DESERT. DAY.   {30}

A rifle shot. A camel drops as though its legs were knocked from under it. Tony looks up from the sights as he leans on the roof of Andrew's old Holden. The other camels run with ungainly steps into the distance. Young Aborigines Andrew, Benson and a few others run shouting with delight towards the gigantic carcass.

SCENE 30   EXT. A COMMUNITY CAMPFIRE – WALA WALA. NIGHT.   {31}

A happy crowd sings a lusty version of 'Michael Row the Boat Ashore'. (Note: in the filmed scene they sing 'Onward Christian Soldiers'.) A side of camel roasts among the coals and Tony, as the hunter who made the kill, is briefly a local hero. Among the singers are Andrew, Benson and David. Mannga and Tjulpu are not present. There are plenty of guitars and clapsticks but the didgeridoo is not native to the central desert and isn't played. Poppy leads the singers enthusiastically. Tony makes a surreptitious drinking gesture to Benson, who in turn nudges Andrew. Poppy falls silent as he watches the three steal away towards Andrew's car. He glances at the First and Second Man, silent among the singers.

SCENE 31   INT. THE LIVING ROOM – THE TEACHER'S RESIDENCE. NIGHT.   {32}

Les, Gordon, Farrelly, Charlie and Sarah lounge around the room as cooking sounds come from the kitchen. Kate stands by the kitchen door, wiping her hands with a tea towel. Charlie talks expansively to Gordon and Farrelly. (Note: in the finished film the first two lines of the following speech are voice over for the scene above.)

CHARLIE: There was a boy in Kintore ... caught a lift with his uncle. He was dropped off; ten Ks down the road his uncle has an accident and dies. But there's no such thing as 'an accident' in local cosmology. Every death is a murder, whether it's done with a ... with a spear or with ... traditional magic. So they blamed the boy ... even though he wasn't in the car at the time. If someone dies around here, they ... they – you know, they always find a culprit.

GORDON: Not exactly fair, though, is it?

CHARLIE: [*smiling*] Maybe. I don't make moral judgements about it.

RAY: Gotta make moral judgements, mate.

> *The sight of Ray standing at the door stops Les dead in his tracks. Sarah smiles at him.*

They make moral judgements about you all the time.

Farrelly makes himself useful pulling chairs around the dining table.

SARAH: Hi, Ray.
RAY: Not late, am I?
KATE: No, no.

Ray is already fortified, but he's cheerful rather than drunk. Kate kisses him on the cheek. Les watches, quietly fuming. Gordon looks at Ray a little warily. Ray smiles.

RAY: [*to Farrelly*] Found your binoculars, by the way.

He produces a leather strap to which a single eyepiece is attached. Farrelly stares at the dangling remains.

FARRELLY: Thanks.
RAY: No trouble.
KATE: [*to all*] Shall we be seated?

As people take their seats Ray draws Les aside.

RAY: Les ... Dave thinks I was a bit out of line the other day. So ...

Les looks him up and down, then glances at his other guests.

LES: Let's say no more about it, shall we?
RAY: Suits me.
LES: I haven't forgotten. But I accept your apology.

Les abruptly joins the others. Ray hesitates a moment, then takes a seat next to Sarah, who puts a hand on his shoulder. Kate smiles at him and he grins back briefly.

LES: Would anyone like another glass of cordial?

SCENE 32   EXT. THE DESERT. NIGHT.   {33}

Tony mimes firing a shotgun, followed by the spraying of liberated beer.

TONY: Pow, pow. Kushhh ... [*Indicating the remaining carton of VBs*] That all I got left.

> *Tony, Andrew and Benson lie without a fire amid the ghostly spinifex and termite mounds. The lights of the settlement are visible nearby and Gospel songs come to them clearly over the night breeze. They are all half drunk. (Note: in the filmed scene Andrew's lines are spoken by Benson.)*

ANDREW: [*miming a shotgun*] Palaru tiwupu nganampa wama. ['He shot up our grog, eh?']
BENSON: He bastard, that one.
TONY: I tell 'im ... I say, he don't tell us what to do.
BENSON: Yuwa. We growed up, eh? Ngaa nganana wangkangu palunyayatula palyrunula.* ['We say what we'll do and we do it.']

> *They all swig their cans defiantly. Benson turns to Tony with a lecherous grin.*

You got ngilpi. Tjurlkura kutju. ['... woman. White one.'] White one.

> *Tony smiles and makes a dismissive gesture. The others laugh.*

You bad one. Bad boy.

> *The Gospel singing wafts over to them. Tony begins singing a traditional song and the others join in. They start to clap. Tony stands and dances a few steps, the n stops.*

TONY: Can't remember.
BENSON: You dance.
TONY: No. All gone. Ngayulu puluna yangkurunu. ['I can't remember.']

> *Tony stands swaying. The singing continues from the settlement.*

I go lurnti. ['... toilet.']

> *Tony lurches off into the darkness.*

---

* Subtitle required on screen.

{SCENE 33   INT. THE KITCHEN – THE TEACHER'S
RESIDENCE. NIGHT.

*Kate prepares dessert – pudding and ice cream – while Les hovers over
her shoulder. The murmur of conversation can be heard in the next
room.*

LES: How could you invite him here?
KATE: I just thought ... we should. I thought ... it would be nice.
LES: 'It ...' I ... 'Nice'? 'Nice'? I'm ... I'm afraid I feel no obligation
    to be 'nice'.
KATE: Les! Not *tonight*. Please.

     Les stares at her. He's been outmanoeuvred – he doesn't like it.}

SCENE 34   INT. THE LIVING ROOM – THE TEACHER'S
RESIDENCE. NIGHT.   {34}

Around the dining table, Ray is holding court.

RAY: Oh, it's bloody right. We're all treading on eggshells, try'n'a
    keep 'em happy. [*To Gordon and Farrelly*] They're smart, y'see.
    {They're ...} They're ... hunter-gatherers, you know? And ...
    what they've done: they've gathered a handful of white people
    in the middle of the desert. And the thing about white people is:
    you only need a few ... and they can last your whole life.

    *Ironic smiles. Gordon and Farrelly are seeing a different side to
    the man who ordered them out of the station. Les appears and
    Ray includes him in the group. Being a little pissed makes all the
    difference.*

RAY: Everything we've done out here could ... could wash off ...

SCENE 35   EXT. THE COMMUNITY CAMPFIRE – WALA
WALA. NIGHT.   {35}

*Poppy stands with Tjulpu, apart from the campfire and the singers. He
makes a surreptitious finger sign to Tjulpu. Tjulpu is stunned. To be
clear, Poppy makes the sign again. Tjulpu glances out into the desert,*

then back at Poppy. His horror grows. He shakes his head vigorously, but Poppy is implacable. He makes the sign a third time.

RAY: [*voice over*] Like a fresh coat of paint. Someone like Poppy: he never saw a whitefella till he was seventeen. When he was in his twenties he went on raiding parties like anyone else.

SCENE 36   INT. THE LIVING ROOM – THE TEACHER'S
RESIDENCE. NIGHT.   {37 ❊}

Ray leans over to Gordon, who leans back slightly.

RAY: He's killed people.

SCENE 37   INT./EXT. THE KITCHEN – THE TEACHER'S
RESIDENCE. NIGHT.   {37 ❊}

Kate scoops ice cream into a serving bowl. Sarah observes through the living-room door as Kate looks out at Tony's camp: still empty. Sarah smiles and turns back to the group in the living room. Kate listens to the Gospel singing.

RAY: [*out of view*] If he hadn't he wouldn't still be around. You look at him, but you don't think of that.

SCENE 38   EXT. THE DESERT. NIGHT.   {38}

Tony stands pissing into the darkness.

RAY: [*voice over*] You don't think of him as a killer.

> *Tony hears a small sound in the darkness. He looks about: is someone there? A first breath of fear curls down the back of his neck.*

SCENE 39   INT./EXT. THE KITCHEN – THE TEACHER'S
RESIDENCE. NIGHT.   {39}

Suddenly Mannga's face appears at the kitchen window, painted completely white. Kate gasps and takes several steps back. The room is plunged into darkness. Kate escapes into the living room.

SCENE 40   INT. THE LIVING ROOM – THE TEACHER'S RESIDENCE. NIGHT.   {40}

Kate stumbles in to find the dinner party is seated around the eerie light of a substantial birthday cake. Thirty candles are alight. Sonia and Adrian, in pyjamas, stand by the table with a present. Kate watches blankly as the others sing 'Happy Birthday', Les orchestrating the hip-hip-hoorays.*

SARAH: [*to the others*] No one told me!

>   *Kate becomes tearful.*

LES: What's wrong?

KATE: Nothing.

LES: Oh, sweetheart. [*Giving her a chummy hug around the shoulders*] You're thirty. We can't just let it go.

KATE: But I want to! Don't you understand?

>   *Charlie glances at Sarah, who stares at the floor. Gordon watches the others for reactions. Ray watches Les, trying to gauge what's happening.*

SONIA: Don't you like your cake, Mummy?

LES: [*to Sonia*] Of course. She's happy, darling. Sometimes people cry when they're happy.

KATE: [*smiling, to the others*] Yes.

>   {*She reads the home-made card: 'To Mummy, from Sonia, Adrian and Daddy.'*}

LES: It's not a funeral, you know. It's the best time in your life coming up. {You can hear a few doors closing, I know, but ... your life is mapped out for you now. You can see where you're headed.}

>   *She smiles and opens the present to find a warm pair of slippers. She is stunned. The others begin to sense something is really wrong.*

---

* In the filmed scene they sing 'For She's a Jolly Good Fellow'.

You said your feet were cold.

She nods and blinks away the tears.

KATE: Thank you.

She still can't respond. She glances towards the kitchen.

LES: Well ... come on. Blow out the candles.
KATE: Yes, of course.

For some reason she can't. She looks at her new slippers.

At Haast's Bluff one Christmas ... we – we were almost killed.
LES: Well, not ... That's a bit of a ...
KATE: No, we were. There were hundreds of people. Hundreds of them. The women: you could hear them in the mornings, shouting, really screaming. And the drinking started and by afternoon it was ... People kept coming to the door with blood pouring down. We bandaged them up. Then the man who ran the store – Frank – he came and he was bleeding. And a crowd gathered and they wanted him; to kill him. My mum and dad were staying: they didn't know what to think. We just sat there with the crowd outside; black faces everywhere, every window. In the end they went away.

She still can't bring herself to blow out the candles. Les tries to salvage something for the journalists.

LES: But you know ... we are really doing something out here.

The others look at him. An eerie silence has settled. They are all suddenly conscious of the dark expanse of desert beyond the house as the waning candles illuminate their faces.

I mean ... making a difference. Just listen.

The Gospel singing comes faintly to them through the night.

The next generation: they'll be ...
GORDON: What?
LES: Something else again.

SCENE 41   EXT. THE DESERT. NIGHT.   {41}

The singing continues in the distance as Tony wanders back to his companions. Two figures lie prone in the dirt next to the remaining grog.

TONY: Eh. You sleeping?

> *He prods them.*

Wake up. Eh.

> *No result. He shrugs and gets himself another can.*

I can drink alone. Don't need you bastards. Don't need no one for drinking.

> *He takes a swig. Still no answer. He prods the nearest figure.*

Eh. You okay?

> *He rolls the figure over and discovers the face of the Second Man, painted deathly white. Traditional music picks up the rhythm of the Christian hymns. In a moment the Second Man's hands close around Tony's neck. He screams and wrenches himself away. The other figure has risen: it's the First Man, also painted up. Tony turns and runs into the bush.*

SCENE 42   INT./EXT. MONTAGE. NIGHT.   {42 ❈}

Tony sprints, terrified, through the scrub as the singing continues around the campfire and Kate and Les farewell their guests. As Poppy leads the singing he seems to be conducting the chase through the desert, the music bridging the three locations. Tony screams out for Andrew and Benson, but they seem to have vanished. Just as Tony thinks he might have outdistanced his pursuers, he runs into the First Man ahead of him. Tony evades the thrust of his spear and charges off in a different direction. The First and Second Man seem to be herding him away from the lights. The community campfire roars as people tear into morsels of camel.

SCENE 43   EXT. A ROAD – THE DESERT. NIGHT.   {43}

At last Tony catches sight of his objective: Andrew's old Holden.

{TONY: [*calling*] Andrew?

No response.} *He jumps in and starts the car. The First and Second Man arrive in time to see him take off down the road.*

SCENE 44   INT. THE LIVING ROOM – THE TEACHER'S RESIDENCE. NIGHT.

Cleaning up, Kate pops a peanut into her mouth from the remnants in a bowl of nibbles.

SCENE 45   EXT. THE COMMUNITY CAMPFIRE – WALA WALA. NIGHT.   {45}

The singers have moved on to 'Safe In the Arms of Jesus'. (Note: in the filmed sequence they sing 'Abide With Me') {*Poppy glances at David, who is enjoying himself, conducting the music.*} *Many are tucking into chunks of cooked camel.*

SCENE 46   EXT. THE ROAD – THE DESERT. NIGHT.   {46}

The car slows, gradually runs up onto the embankment, continues for a while, then stops. The motor idles.

SCENE 47   INT. THE LIVING ROOM – THE TEACHER'S RESIDENCE. NIGHT.   {44, 47}

Kate is choking. Les appears from the kitchen, concerned, but Kate suddenly manages to cough up the peanut and sucks in a great breath.

SCENE 48   EXT. ANDREW'S CAR – THE DESERT. NIGHT.{48}

The old motor continues to idle unevenly. {*The back door on the driver's side is open. Someone has left the car and vanished into the night.*}

SCENE 49   EXT. THE COMMUNITY CAMPFIRE – WALA WALA. NIGHT.   {49}

Poppy brings the hymn to a close. His expression is in contrast to the happy faces around him. David looks at him, the little cross on his shirt glinting in the firelight.

SCENE 50   INT./EXT. THE KITCHEN – THE TEACHER'S
RESIDENCE. MORNING.   {50}

*Bacon and eggs sizzle on the stove. {Kate puts the cereal bowls in the
sink and runs water on them.} Through the window she sees David
angrily directing her children back towards the house. She grimaces.*

SCENE 51   EXT. THE BACK YARD – THE TEACHER'S
RESIDENCE. MORNING.   {51}

Kate pokes her head from the doorway and calls.

KATE: Tony! Want some ... ?

> *For the first time she realises that, but for the recumbent figure of
> Tony in his bedroll, the place is deserted.*

> *{From a distance David watches:} Kate, a tiny figure next to the
> house, pauses for a long moment. At last she approaches the body.
> She shakes him. He moves limply. She rolls him to face her. A
> few people have gathered near the gate. She calls out:*

Sarah! Sarah! ... Les!

> *A few more people arrive and move hesitantly into the yard.
> {David's view is obscured by a gathering crowd, but he can hear
> Kate scream.}*

No! Get away! Get away from us! Sarah! Get away! Sarah!
Where are you? No, no, no!

> *{David flinches at her cries.} Les enters from the house, but
> keeps his distance. He doesn't notice Adrian and Sonia appear
> behind him.*

> *Kate's point of view: staring faces seem to close in on all sides,
> but there are no cries of grief; only horrid silence.*

Tony! Tony, get up! Get up! Tony, please, no ... Tony, no ...
Please ... Please, Tony ... Please ... [*To the Aborigines*] Get away
... Get away from us ... Tony ...

> *She notices the flash of the Betacam's lens in the crowd.*

Absurdly, Gordon wears nothing but a pair of jeans, and Farrelly only underpants and boots. {A little distance away David approaches, grim like all the rest.} Kate suddenly realises that she is screaming.

SCENE 52   INT. THE CONSULTING ROOM – THE CLINIC.
DAY.   {52}

Silence. Tony's body lies on its back on a surgical table, half covered by a sheet. There is something touching about his clothes, neatly folded and stacked on top of a plastic garbage bag. Sarah and Ray sit quietly nearby amid the white walls and well-used equipment.

RAY: 'A heart attack'?
SARAH: It does happen. Even to young men.

> *Ray looks at her doubtfully, then stands and moves Tony's head back and forth, examining his neck.*

There's not a mark on him; no bruises, no puncture wounds, nothing.

> *Ray sighs. He runs a hand gently through Tony's hair.*

RAY: Silly bugger.

> *He takes Tony's shoes from the pile of clothes. He looks tired.*

I'll get Dave.

> *Sarah stands and pulls the sheet over Tony's face.*

SARAH: When's Billy get back?
RAY: Today, I hope. He'll have a limp, apparently. Permanent.
SARAH: Oh, God.

> *Ray stares at the shrouded, silent form on the table. He feels a sudden stab of anger.*

RAY: Yeah.

> *He leaves. Sarah stares at the body.*

SCENE 53   INT./EXT. THE BULK FREEZER – THE STORE.
DAY.   {53}

David and Ray carry the body into the freezer. David has changed his clothes but still looks very drawn. The freezer is the size of a small room; it's well stocked and there's very little space.

DAVID: Next to the kangaroo tails.

> *They move the body past piles of cardboard boxes and lay it down next to half a dozen long packages labelled 'Roo/T'. Ray can't help grinning.*

What?
RAY: Nothing.

> *Ray looks out at the petrol sniffer and a few children, standing in the dust, watching. He is about to clear them off when he notices Gordon and Farrelly behind them.*

What're they doing here?

> *Gordon takes out a folded sheet of paper and waves it cheerfully.*

DAVID: Oh ... They've been approved.
RAY: What? By who?
DAVID: Poppy, um ...
RAY: Fuckin' great.

> *Farrelly tries to take a shot of what they're doing, but a figure among the onlookers gestures angrily at him. Farrelly lowers the camera.*

DAVID: They'll want some kind of statement.
RAY: Yeah, bugger 'em.
DAVID: [*contemplating the body*] How long d'you want to keep it here?
RAY: Till I can drive it in. Probably tomorrow.

> *They step out into the sun and close the freezer door. David takes a closer look at the figure who waved at Farrelly: the First Man. David can't work out whether he recognises him or not, but it's a disturbing sight. He turns to the matter at hand.*

DAVID: Ray ...
RAY: What?

> *Ray brushes a fly from his face. An eerie silence has descended on the community. Ray looks at him, taking in his entire appearance.*

You look a bit tired, Dave.

> *David looks away. Ray looks at the onlookers, about to clear them off, when he notices a familiar face. He grins.*

Hey, Billy.

> *Billy hobbles towards him. Ray's face falls as he sees Billy's painful walk. He recovers in a moment and walks heartily over to meet him.*

SCENE 54   INT. THE CLASSROOM – THE SCHOOL. DAY.{54}

Les sits behind the desk. Adrian and Sonia are alone in class.

LES: Open your Geography books, kids.

> *They open their books. Les pulls down a map of Australia. His eyes are drawn into the great blank space in the centre: the dead heart.*

SCENE 55   EXT. THE BACK YARD – THE TEACHER'S RESIDENCE. DAY.   {55}

David holds Tony's shoes, which seem remarkably heavy. Ray looks over Billy's shoulder at the area where the crowd gathered.

BILLY: Just a big mess here, boss. [*Indicating a spot further away*] But here: good one.

> *He takes one of the shoes from David and holds it above a footprint: a sliver broken off the heel matches the track exactly. He points out the gait of several prints.*

He been pretty drunk, I reckon. [*Making 'drunk' motions with his hands*] He been this one. [*Going down on one knee*] He go down this one. Then he fall down, been sleep, I reckon.

> *Ray glances at David, who indicates that it sounds plausible.*
> *Behind David, Ray notices Poppy, shaded from view, watching*
> *them closely from the front seat of his derelict Toyota. Ray stares*
> *back.*

DAVID: [*to Ray*] What're you thinking?

SCENE 56   INT. THE OFFICE – THE POLICE STATION.
NIGHT.   {56}

(Note: for logistical reasons, in the finished film night falls at Scene 81.)
A video image: in slow motion, eerily silent, Aboriginal legs move
aside to reveal Tony's body cradled in Kate's arms. Ray is watching
Farrelly's tape recorded earlier that day.

SCENE 57   EXT. THE POLICE COMPOUND – WALA WALA.
NIGHT.   {57}

Farrelly paces resentfully back and forth outside the station.

SCENE 58   INT. THE OFFICE – THE POLICE STATION.
NIGHT.   {58}

On the tape Gordon is briefly visible clearing people from view. The
body sags from side to side as Kate rocks. Ray's eyes narrow as he sees
David arrive, calm but grim.

{RAY: [*softly*] You ... bastard.}

SCENE 59   INT. THE KITCHEN – THE DOCTOR'S
RESIDENCE. NIGHT.   {59, 60 ✳, 61 ✳}

(Note: the intercutting of the following sequence varies significantly in
the finished film.) Sarah sits with a mug of tea and lights a cigarette as
Charlie carves up great hunks of camel meat and drops the slices into
three eskies.

{SARAH: I started smoking again.

CHARLIE: You'll give up.
SARAH: God you're good.

> *He gives her a hands-free kiss on the cheek. Sarah smiles and glances through the kitchen window at Kate, who sits on the dirt-floored verandah clutching half a cup of tea as she stares fearfully out into the shadows. Sarah turns to Charlie.*}

Can't you do this later? The place smells like an abattoir.
CHARLIE: Sorry. Don't want it to go off.

> *Sarah looks at him ruefully.*

How's Kate?
SARAH: Pretty poor.
CHARLIE: She's not taken it well.

SCENE 60   INT. THE OFFICE – THE POLICE STATION.
NIGHT.   {60 ✻, 62 ✻}

Ray watches the video. Farrelly's camera has focussed on Kate as she rocks, still in slow motion, her face a portrait of utter despair.

SARAH: [*voice over*] Well ... how'd you like to find me dead one
    morning?
CHARLIE: [*voice over*] Oh, sure, but that's not ...

SCENE 61   INT. THE KITCHEN – THE DOCTOR'S
RESIDENCE. NIGHT.   {63 ✻}

The penny drops. Sarah shakes her head in mock disbelief.

{SARAH: Some anthropologist.}
CHARLIE: She was having an affair?
SARAH: Of course she was having an affair.

SCENE 62   INT. THE OFFICE – THE POLICE STATION.
NIGHT.   {63 ✻}

The video screen shows Kate with the body. By now Sarah has opened her medical bag and is saying something to Kate. Ray can see himself clearing people away, including Gordon and the camera. Les hovers ineffectually but Kate is inconsolable. She is screaming something into the empty desert.

{CHARLIE: [*voice over*] Kate?
SARAH: [*voice over*] Yes.
CHARLIE: [*voice over*] With Tony?
SARAH: [*voice over*] Yes.}

SCENE 63   INT. THE KITCHEN – THE DOCTOR'S RESIDENCE. NIGHT.   {64, 65 ✲, 66}

Sarah smiles at Charlie's consternation. Annoyed, he goes back to his carving. What's worse, Sarah seems to like the idea.

CHARLIE: Just ... surprising.
SARAH: They used to meet at that waterhole. Malley Creek.

> *Charlie shrugs.*

CHARLIE: Well, she better not ...

> *Suddenly it hits him. He turns to her.*

When?

SCENE 64   INT. THE OFFICE – THE POLICE STATION. NIGHT.   {65 ✲}

Ray leans forward, adjusts the video to normal speed, and turns up the sound. Kate's voice comes over clearly.

KATE: Get away from us! Get away! No, no ... Get away from us!

SCENE 65   INT. THE LIVING ROOM – THE DOCTOR'S RESIDENCE. NIGHT.   {67 ✲}

(Note: only the dialogue from this scene was retained in the finished film.) Billy stands at Charlie's desk examining a topographical map marked in many colours with lines and detailed notes: a record of the local Dreaming. Outside he can faintly hear Ray's voice.

RAY: [*out of view*] Kate ... are you frightened about something? Is that it? If you are you have to tell me. Otherwise I can't help.

SCENE 66 EXT. THE VERANDAH – THE DOCTOR'S RESIDENCE. NIGHT. {67 *}

Kate stares at Ray, who squats before her in a bushman's crouch.

RAY: [*gently*] I know ... he was more than a friend. Wasn't he?

Suddenly tears well in her eyes. She leans forward, then notices Les approaching. She turns and escapes into the house. Ray swears under his breath.

Hi, Les.
LES: Hello.

Les follows Kate into the house. Ray follows.

SCENE 67 INT. THE LIVING ROOM – THE DOCTOR'S RESIDENCE. NIGHT. {68}

Billy turns as Charlie and Sarah enter from the kitchen. He is now somewhat cleaned up, though still spotted with blood. Sarah begins to close the kitchen door as Kate enters.

SARAH: Sorry about the ... [smell.]

Kate brushes past Sarah and goes into the kitchen. Les enters from the verandah, followed by Ray. Sarah glances at the two men, hesitates a moment, then follows Kate. Ray stares after her, frustration building. Billy turns back to the Dreaming map.

BILLY: [*following a purple line marked 'Tingarri Dreaming' with his finger*] Tingarri one.
CHARLIE: [*a little surprised*] Um ... yes, that's right.

Pause. Charlie attempts a salvage of some kind.

Where's your Dreaming, Billy?
BILLY: Not here. I got Tiger Dreaming.
CHARLIE: Tiger?

BILLY: Yeah. You know: [*miming a football*] Richmond.

Charlie and Les laugh. Ray grins. Billy is annoyed.

What you laughing?

CHARLIE: I'm sorry. I'm sorry.

BILLY: You watpalla funny bugger.

Charlie stifles his laughter. Suddenly they are aware that Les is sobbing into his hands. An excruciating moment. At last Les controls himself. He takes a step towards the kitchen.

LES: I think we'll be getting along if you don't mind.

CHARLIE: Stay for a bit, Les. Have a cup of tea.

LES: No, no. See to the children.

Kate appears from the kitchen, followed by Sarah.

Oh. Sweetheart. I was just saying we should pop off home.

KATE: Were you, darling?

Kate looks him in the eyes and touches his cheek, leaving an imprint of camel blood. She walks out. Les wipes his face with a handkerchief.

LES: You spend your whole life ...

He looks at the others, then follows Kate. Sarah goes to the door and stares after them: two lonely figures being swallowed by the night.

RAY: [*to Sarah*] What's going on?

Sarah hesitates.

SARAH: I'm ... not sure.

RAY: Come on, Sarah: what'd she say?

SARAH: Nothing.

RAY: You've been with her all day; she said something.

Sarah hesitates.

CHARLIE: Ray ...

RAY: What?

CHARLIE: You're acting like a policeman.

RAY: I am a policeman.

CHARLIE: She doesn't know anything.

> *Ray stares at him.*

RAY: Doesn't she? What about you?

> *Charlie hesitates.*

Come on, Charlie. Come outside.

CHARLIE: What?

RAY: Come and have a chat. Billy: stay with Sarah.

SCENE 68   EXT. DOCTOR'S RESIDENCE – WALA WALA. NIGHT.   {69, 71}

(Note: in the finished film this scene is divided by an unscripted interior Scene 70 in which Billy and Sarah overhear the conversation.) Charlie follows Ray. He feels stupid.

CHARLIE: Ray ... there's nothing to discuss.

RAY: What she say to you, Charlie? You can tell me; it's alright.

CHARLIE: She didn't say anything.

RAY: You wouldn't lie to me, would you? Or conceal anything?

CHARLIE: No.

> *Ray looks at him for a moment.*

RAY: Course you would, Charlie: you're an anthropologist. {You think people should ... should live according to their culture.} If Tony was knocked off for some tribal reason, you'd hide it from me; am I right?

> *Pause.*

CHARLIE: I – I – I – Ray ...

RAY: Alright, how would you feel about a charge of concealing a murder?

CHARLIE: What?

RAY: I'm not joking.

CHARLIE: I know.

RAY: Because that's what you'll get. If you're concealing something. Think about it. Your grant money. The work you're doing. Might even do time. I'll do it: I'll nail you to the wall. I bend the law a hell of a lot so we can do things tribal way. But if I turn a blind eye to this ... I might as well not be here. Come on, Charlie: you know something. You look like a fart on it's way out.

CHARLIE: [*laughing stupidly*] Ray ... it's nothing.

RAY: In that case it can't hurt, can it?

CHARLIE: These people have just let me in ...

RAY: I know. I know that, Charlie. It'll be okay; don't worry.

> *Charlie stares at him hopelessly. Suddenly Ray is aware of Sarah watching from the verandah.*

CHARLIE: Sarah said ... said ... Tony took Kate to the business ground. To Malley Creek.

RAY: He ... And ... she saw the – the ... Did she see the stuff there?

CHARLIE: Well, it ... I don't know! She ... Sarah told me: go and ask her, for God sake!

RAY: Couldn't do that, mate. She wouldn't tell me. Billy!

SCENE 69   EXT. WALA WALA. NIGHT.   {72}

Climactic choral music. Ray strides towards David's house.

BILLY: Eh, boss!

RAY: What?

BILLY: More better this one been tribal way.

> *Ray ignores him. The music bridges to:*

SCENE 70   INT./EXT. THE STUDY – THE COMMUNITY ADVISER'S RESIDENCE. NIGHT.   {73}

David looks up from his desk as Ray enters.

DAVID: [*shouting over the music*] Sorry. I'm writing a sermon.

RAY: Sounds like you're gunna clout 'em this week.

> *David stands and turns the music off. Ray picks up a brochure on David's desk: 'Aboriginal and Torres Strait Islanders' Commission'. He flips through it. Billy enters.*

Thing is, I'm after some advice.

Ray tosses the brochure onto the desk. David sits. Billy looks nervously from one to another.

I've done some thinking in my ... quiet, plodding way. Come up with a theory about Tony. My theory goes like this: Tony was killed for fucking his girlfriend on a sacred site. What d'you think?

Pause.

DAVID: It's, um ...

RAY: Let me spell it out a bit. He takes this girl to a business ground; the old men find out. They have him killed out bush somewhere ... they sing his spirit out. Then they take his shoes off. They put him in his bedroll. Someone uses the shoes to make the tracks leading to the body ... {and they put them back on his feet.} And Kate finds him next day. As a warning. 'Cause she was the one he was with. What d'you reckon? Hold water?

DAVID: Ray ... You can't *make* someone die of a heart attack.

RAY: [*wandering around behind David*] Oh, you'd be surprised. There's a way of killing a man by ... [*flexing the crook of his elbow around David's neck*] blocking both arteries in the neck. The old ones know about it. Do it right, there's a ...

Ray jerks his elbow. David jumps and grabs Ray's arm.

Reflex stoppage of the heart. [*Releasing him*] Yeah, I never seen it, but I've heard about it.

David takes a moment to steady his breathing.

DAVID: Poppy might say, 'Kudaitcha man'.

RAY: [*crossing to the window*] I bet he would. I bet he'd say all kinds of spooky stuff. But I don't believe in that. I think the old men commissioned a young bloke from around here. Someone really strong in his culture. What d'you think?

DAVID: I ... I don't know.

RAY: Don't you? I'm curious to know, Dave ... how come you stopped Kate's kids from finding the body.

DAVID: I ... Did I?

RAY: Yeah, you knew he was dead. I've seen a video of you arriving on the scene, Dave; Kate screaming her head off: you're not alarmed. You know.

> *Pause.*

That's right, Dave. I'm giving you a chance. {Like you gave me.} [*Picking up the brochure*] ATSIC for you, wasn't it? Ladder up the public service? You better work out your priorities, boy.

DAVID: I don't ...

RAY: Don't what?

DAVID: Why are you doing this?

RAY: My job, Dave. Have to do my *job*, don't I?

> *Then comes Poppy's song: an insistent murmur, almost under the breath. Ray looks around, as though Poppy were just behind him.*

I put it this way: this dirty little hole is my Dreaming. Charlie should put it on his map: 'Ray's Dreaming'. I belong here. [*Stabbing a finger at the window*] And that old bastard ... wants to get rid of me because I sent him down for shooting up his own Toyota. I mean: is that a joke?

DAVID: Poppy?

RAY: Who do you think? He wants my blood. He's singing me now.

> *He listens.*

Can't you hear it?

> *David shakes his head. Ray goes to the window and looks out.*

It's him or me, Dave. Him or me.

SCENE 71   EXT. WALA WALA. NIGHT.   {74}

Poppy sees Ray's distant silhouette in the window of David's study. Poppy punctuates his murmuring song with sharp breaths over his hands which send its message to Ray.

RAY: [*voice over*] And if he ... instructed – if he *sanctioned* this killing ... it's gunna be him. He's going away.

SCENE 72   INT. THE STUDY – THE COMMUNITY
ADVISER'S RESIDENCE. NIGHT.   {75}

Ray can still hear the song. He leans across David's desk.

RAY: And you're gunna help me.

DAVID: Ray ... I can't.

RAY: Then someone else will. And you'll be an accessory. That'll
    be the end of your contribution to Aboriginal wealth and
    culture. So what's it to be? I'd like to let you off the hook but
    my hands are tied. I'm just doing a job, aren't I, Bill?

BILLY: You do it good, Ray.

RAY: [*to David*] There you go. So come on: what d'you say?

DAVID: I thought we were friends.

RAY: We are.

DAVID: You're a prick.

RAY: That's a bit rugged from a man of the cloth, Dave. A pastor
    like yourself ... protecting a murderer. Don't you worry about
    that? I mean, what would God think? Doesn't really sit too
    well, does it?

DAVID: You – Don't you think I've thought of that?

RAY: Have you? Thought of what?

    Pause.

Thought of what, Dave?

    Pause.

Well, well.

DAVID: He did it.

RAY: What was that?

DAVID: He did it. Alright? Tjulpu killed him. It's tribal business;
    it's got nothing to do with you. Why don't you stay out of the
    whole fucking thing, {watpalla.}

RAY: [*smiling*] Thanks, mate.

SCENE 73   EXT. POPPY'S BACK YARD – WALA WALA.
NIGHT.   {14, 76}

Mannga and other members of his family sit around a fire. He is finishing off a new spear, hardening it over the fire. Tjulpu sits alone, hugging his knees and nursing a secret sadness into which the others do not intrude. (Note: in the film the opening of this scene is used to establish Mannga and Tjulpu in the settlement after the payback.) Tjulpu looks up, suddenly aware of Ray approaching on foot, Billy following at his hobbling pace.

RAY: [*to Tjulpu*] You're in all sorts of shit, boy.

> *Ray slaps one end of his handcuffs onto Tjulpu's right wrist. Tjulpu pulls away angrily and Ray hits him in the face. Tjulpu falls like a log. A roar of protest goes up and people begin to arrive from all sides. Mannga, enraged, grabs his spear and drops into a fighting stance, only to find himself staring down the barrel of Ray's pistol. The shouting dies as bystanders scamper out of the line of fire.*

[*to Mannga*] Yeah? Yeah? Come on.

> *Silence. The two men stare each other down. Suddenly Poppy grasps Mannga's spear-throwing wrist. Mannga looks at him with surprise: no one saw him arrive. Ray doesn't take his eyes from Mannga.*

Billy!

BILLY: Yeh.

RAY: [*indicating Tjulpu*] Put the cuffs on him.

> *Billy shifts uneasily. Ray realises his order is not being carried out.*

Billy!

BILLY: [*indicating Tjulpu*] That one my tjampati.

{RAY: He's your *what*?

BILLY: He's Tjangala, I'm Tjapaltjarri. I can't —} I can't touch him, boss.

RAY: You can't *touch* him?

BILLY: Wrong skin name.

RAY: 'Wrong skin name?' Billy ... that is not what I want to hear right now.

*Billy's embarrassment is excruciating. Ray keeps one eye on
Mannga and looks around at the hostile crowd with the other.
Tjulpu is rapidly recovering. Ray pushes the pistol into Billy's
unwilling hands.*

Hold this.

*Billy holds the pistol awkwardly. As one the bystanders move
further back. Ray turns Tjulpu over roughly and secures the
handcuffs, then drags him up. He takes the gun from Billy.
Someone shoves Billy from behind and he turns with a raised fist
but Ray pulls him back.*

SCENE 74   EXT. WALA WALA. NIGHT.   {77}

*Ray, Tjulpu and a terrified Billy head for the lock-up, followed by the
angry, shouting crowd. Ray refuses to hurry, fear building to rage.*

SCENE 75   EXT. THE POLICE COMPOUND – WALA WALA.
NIGHT.   {78}

*The three reach the compound and Ray locks the gate. He, Billy and
Tjulpu disappear inside the station. The angry crowd pick up anything
they can find and start to bash the fence around the police compound.*

SCENE 76   INT. THE STORE ROOM – THE POLICE
STATION. NIGHT.   {79}

*With fumbling fingers Ray breaks open the weapons cabinet. He is
blind with fury now, barely rational. He grabs his shotgun.*

SCENE 77   INT. THE MUSTER ROOM – THE POLICE
STATION. NIGHT.   {80}

Billy trembles as Ray passes him and Tjulpu on his way to the door.

SCENE 78   EXT. THE POLICE STATION – WALA WALA.
NIGHT.   {81}

*Ray points the shotgun at the angry crowd. Behind the fence people
duck for cover. Silence.*

RAY: [*pointing at Poppy*] What d'you want from me? Eh? Don't I do everything right way? Take your kids to hospital Alice Springs? Teach you to drive? Keep the grog out, don't I? Stop your women getting bashed up? Wala Wala way: that's *my* way. That's *my* way and I tell you what: I never said to kill someone.

> *The crowd is a little uncertain. No one quite follows what he is on about. Ray spots Poppy amongst the others. Their eyes lock.*

Well ... things are gunna change around here. I let you do things tribal way before, but ... we're gunna tighten up now, don't you worry. You treat me like watpalla I show you watpalla way, don't you fuckin' worry.

> *Ray goes inside and slams the door. A spear clatters to the ground. On the fringe of the crowd, Farrelly lowers his camera and gazes, wide-eyed, at Gordon .*

GORDON: What was all that about?
FARRELLY: Who gives a *fuck?* It was *fuckin' great!*

SCENE 79   INT./ EXT. THE MUSTER ROOM – THE POLICE STATION. NIGHT.   {82}

Angry shouts can be heard outside. Ray looks about and his eyes light on the handcuffed Tjulpu. Billy stands to one side. Swinging the shotgun, Ray approaches Tjulpu, who remains defiant.

RAY: You piece of shit.

> *Billy intervenes, standing between Ray and the object of his wrath.*

BILLY: Boss ...

> *Ray doesn't move. His eyes are fixed on Tjulpu.*

I put 'im – I put 'im lock-up. Okay?
RAY: I'm gunna —
BILLY: [*interrupting*] I put him lock-up. Right now, eh? You wait. I put him now. Okay? [*Taking the keys from the desk*] He been settle down. Quiet as a mouse, boss. You wait.

Without speaking to or looking directly at Tjulpu, Billy manages to herd him through the store room. Through the window Ray sees Tjulpu and Billy approach the lock-up. Ray seems to lose momentum. Billy and Tjulpu reach the door and Tjulpu will go no further.

TJULPU: Wiya ... Wiya!

Hampered by the skin taboo, Billy is caught in an impossible dilemma. Ray points the shotgun through the window.

RAY: Eh! Kumatjila, minipuka! ['Come on, fucking cunt!']

SCENE 80   EXT. THE LOCK-UP – THE POLICE STATION. NIGHT.   {83}

Tjulpu and Billy see the shotgun at the same moment. Billy snaps. His fear and frustration explode as he hits Tjulpu hard from behind, then drags him, thrashing and yelling, into the lock-up. Billy subdues him with several swift kicks, then runs out, slams the door and locks it.

ABORIGINAL GIRL: Eh! He been lock-up!

Billy realises that he's been observed. The crowd follows the girl around and Tjulpu glimpses them through the mesh. They shout abuse at Billy, who sways on the bars, appalled by his own actions.

SCENE 81   INT. THE MUSTER ROOM – THE POLICE STATION. NIGHT.   {84}

Billy quietly puts the keys away. Ray watches him, still clutching the shotgun. Billy has crossed some kind of line now and there may be no way back.

BILLY: You do it good, Ray. No worries.

Ray looks at him.

[*putting a hand on the shotgun*] You give me this one.

Ray pulls away. Pause. Billy tries another tack.

You give me beer.

RAY: You want a beer?
BILLY: Yeah.
RAY: Get me one too.

> *Ray sits with the shotgun between his knees. Billy fetches the two beers. Ray cracks his and takes a swig. Billy stands watching him, the unopened can in his hand. Ray looks up at him, slightly uncomfortable.*

Get some rest.
BILLY: Oh ... I been wake up too much. I sit here little bit.

> *Ray looks at him a moment.*

RAY: [*softly*] Okay ...

> *Billy sits down gently and prepares to watch him for the rest of the night. After a moment they hear a distant, mournful song. Ray doesn't react, but for Billy the sound is profoundly disturbing. He glances through the window into the black shadows of the lock-up. The music bridges:*

SCENE 82   INT. THE CONSULTING ROOM – THE CLINIC. DAY.   {85}

Sarah stares through the window of the clinic. She glances at the clock: after nine; then looks at the examination table where Tony lay only a few hours ago.

SCENE 83   INT. THE BULK FREEZER – THE STORE. DAY.{86}

The door of the freezer meditates on the body it hides. At a little distance Benson is the only, silent mourner. Faintly he can hear the compressors running.

SCENE 84   INT. THE MUSTER ROOM – THE POLICE STATION. DAY.   {87}

A video viewfinder wobbles as it tries to find framing and focus. Several voices, however, are quite distinct.

RAY: [*out of view*] What'd Poppy have to say?

GORDON: [*out of view*] Oh, he um ... He's got his own ... unique perspective. He painted you as a very colourful character.

RAY: Did he just?

The camera zooms in, focuses, zooms out. Ray is now framed neatly in the viewfinder. He hasn't slept, but has combed his hair and looks presentable.

GORDON: [*out of view*] You right?

Ray nods. Gordon puts on his official voice.

[*out of view*] Senior constable, how much contact has Mr Tjangala had with white society?

RAY: I wouldn't know.

GORDON: [*out of view*] Well, he ... he doesn't speak English. He's being held under a law he's never heard of. Is that fair?

RAY: {Well, that ... We're} ... The law ... has to apply equally to everyone.

GORDON: [*out of view*] Equal ... but not necessarily fair.

Ray hesitates. The camera begins a slow zoom in.

[*out of view*] Well, if ... Mr Tjangala's had no contact with white law, his father was not so lucky: he died in police custody. In fact, in your custody.

Something inside Ray begins to churn. He tries to hide it from the camera, but it seeps through.

RAY: Yes. That's correct.

GORDON: [*out of view*] Would you say he received equal treatment?

RAY: Yes.

GORDON: [*out of view*] It's Aboriginal custom to avoid places where ... where death has occurred. Where family have died. But Mr Tjangala is now being held in the same cell his father died in a few months ago. How do you think he feels?

RAY: {He would ... It's not —} It's unfortunate, but it's the only cell we have.

GORDON: [*out of view*] Isn't it possible he might kill himself?

No answer. The shot is very tight. Ray lets the silence drag on.

[*out of view*] Senior constable, why are you still here?

> *Again the silence drags on.*

[*out of view, softly*] Cut.

> *The television image hovers for a moment, then the record light blinks off and the screen goes blank.*

> *Ray remains in his seat for a few moments as Gordon and Farrelly pack up wordlessly. Ray stands and takes Gordon's arm.*

RAY: [*to Farrelly*] Won't be a tick. Just want a word.

> *Ray manhandles Gordon through the door to the store room. Farrelly goes to follow and finds the solid figure of Billy blocking his way.*

BILLY: [*to Farrelly*] You: sit. Camera finish.

SCENE 85   INT. THE STORE ROOM – THE POLICE STATION. DAY.   {88}

Ray has Gordon cornered between two banks of steel shelves. There's nowhere to run and Gordon is more than a little nervous.

RAY: Been doing this long, have you? Professional arsehole?
GORDON: Well ... what's your problem, Ray?

> *Ray shoves him hard. Gordon recovers his balance, but now he's really scared.*

RAY: You know, in the old days, if the blackfellas killed a bloke they weren't meant to ... they'd dig a hole in a termite mound, put the body in. Few hours the termites'd fix up the hole, body would never be found.
GORDON: What's that supposed to mean?
RAY: You're a journalist. Why don't you figure it out?

> {*Outside, the telephone rings. Gordon glances towards the sound.*} *Ray doesn't move. Gordon hesitates, then gingerly squeezes past. To his relief he emerges unscathed and, marshalling what dignity he can, opens the door and exits to the muster room.*

SCENE 86   EXT. THE POLICE COMPOUND – WALA WALA. DAY.   {89}

The settlement appears deserted under the harsh light. Tjulpu's mournful song floats from the dark hole of the lock-up. The gate of the compound is back in its usual position: open. The settlement seems deserted. David, carrying a briefcase, strides towards the station. He passes Gordon and Farrelly who are on their way out. Gordon looks very rattled. Ray ambles out to meet him.

RAY: What d'you want?

DAVID: Talk to the prisoner.

RAY: Oh, him. Think you'll convert 'im?

DAVID: You'd be surprised.

RAY: I hear Balgo every year they dance the Stations of the Cross. They really get into the taunting. That's their favourite bit, the taunting.

DAVID: We should've got him back in the desert.

RAY: Bit late for that, mate. He's a killer.

DAVID: He didn't have a choice. {If he … Assuming he did it …}

RAY: Not in my book. In my book you always got a choice.

    Pause.

DAVID: I've rung Legal Aid. I want to tell him what's going on.

RAY: Okay.

DAVID: Are they sending a plane?

RAY: Yeah, day or two. {[*Glaring into the endless desert*] There's a search on for some stupid dick.}

    David looks at him.

DAVID: You look like shit, by the way.

RAY: Least I'm not the same colour.

    They smile briefly for the friendship that was.

SCENE 87   INT./ EXT. THE LOCK-UP – WALA WALA. DAY. {90}

Tjulpu's song trails off as Billy sleepily unlocks the door to let David in. Inside the door is a plate of stale sandwiches. Tjulpu turns and looks up from his cross-legged position in the corner of the cell. It's a shocking transformation. Wrapped in a grey blanket, he looks drawn and tormented. David looks at Billy, who turns away, ashamed, and trudges back to the station. {David glances out beyond the wire where Poppy watches silently. He turns back and smiles encouragingly at Tjulpu as} he opens his briefcase. Hidden inside is a noose of thick rope.

SCENE 88   INT. THE MAIN BEDROOM – THE TEACHER'S
RESIDENCE. DAY.   {91}

Still in her nightgown Kate stares out the window as Les puts on a fresh shirt. {The old one lies crumpled on the bed.}

LES: There's no one out there.

KATE: I can – I can feel ...

LES: No, no. There's no one there. [*Checking his appearance in a full-length mirror*] It's important, though, we shouldn't waver. They'll be back. As long as we stand firm. Tony would've wanted us to —

KATE: [*interrupting*] How can you say what Tony would've wanted?

LES: I beg your pardon.

KATE: You didn't know Tony, what he thought, what ... what he could do.

LES: I think I knew him a little better than you.

KATE: Why? Did you fuck him?

Les is struck dumb. Kate turns back to the window.

LES: I don't know you. I don't know you at all.

KATE: No.

Pause.

LES: I imagine ... I imagine ... you were in love with him, were you? It was love, was it?

KATE: No.

LES: Not love?

KATE: No.

LES: Lust, then?

KATE: I don't know. Yes. I don't know. Les ... something ... that he had, some ... knowledge that he had; Les ... I've seen the place ... where little boys die ... and become men.

Les looks at her, disturbed.

And ... I'm afraid.

Pause. He shakes his head.

LES: Oh, no. No, no.
KATE: People here ... know what I've done.
LES: No. No!
KATE: Les —
LES: [*interrupting*] No, I won't let you do this.

Kate stares at him.

We moved on from Hermannsburg and Haast's Bluff because you couldn't cope; I won't move on from here. I love it. I love what we're doing, I love these people, I love this land, I love everything about it. This is home for me. I won't give it up; do you hear me?
KATE: [*screaming*] I hate it here! I hate it! I hate these dirty, dumpy little places. I hate their ugliness. I hate these people, I hate ... touching them. I hate their smell. I hate their hands and their ... fetid breath. They're ugly, dirty black animals. They're boongs. Coons. Niggers. They should be rounded up and shot; they should be exterminated. They should be ... hunted like ...

Les stares at her.

Oh, God ... [*Reaching out*] Les ...

He pulls away. Kate notices Sonia at the door.

LES: [*to Kate*] I have a class.

He goes to the door and picks up his daughter.

I think, under the circumstances, we'll tough it out, don't you?

SCENE 89   INT./EXT. THE LOCK-UP – WALA WALA. NIGHT.   {92}

Tjulpu watches the police station closely as he sings his despair. Despite his blanket he shivers uncontrollably. A rope creaks and for a moment his father's cowboy boot might be lying on the floor. But no: it's a shadow. Above him the noose is secured to a grille near the ceiling.

SCENE 90   INT./EXT. THE MUSTER ROOM – THE POLICE STATION. NIGHT.   {93}

Beer in hand, Billy watches the Tigers play on television. The phone rings and he picks it up automatically.

BILLY: Yuwa ... Yeah? What your name? ... *Kidney Morning Herald*? ... Newspaper: okay.
ABORIGINAL MAN: [*out of view, faintly*] Eh! Constable! Eh! You come! Constable!

> *Still on the phone, Billy turns to the window and sees Tjulpu hanging by the noose. He drops everything and grabs the keys from the desk.*

SCENE 91   EXT. THE POLICE COMPOUND – WALA WALA. NIGHT.   {94}

(Note: the filmed scene contains some changes. The rope is tied in such a way that Tjulpu is never in danger. Billy realises this just before the punch.) Three men hover about the lock-up as Billy charges over. He unlocks the door and, as he can't touch his tjampati, ushers two of the men inside. They throw themselves under Tjulpu and lower him to the ground. He lies there, gasping. Billy cries out with relief: a repetition of the nightmare has been averted. The third man gives Billy a friendly slap on the shoulder and punches him across the mouth.

SCENE 92   INT. THE BEDROOM – THE POLICE RESIDENCE. NIGHT.   {95}

In bed, though still half dressed, Ray drags himself to consciousness. Something is roaring at him. It is a few seconds before he realises it is the police vehicle, revving its guts out. He starts, suddenly fully awake.

SCENE 93   EXT. THE POLICE COMPOUND – WALA WALA.
NIGHT.   {96}

*Ray emerges from the house, buckling his pants. The police vehicle,
with Tjulpu and his three rescuers inside, is doing doughnuts around
the station, amid whoops and laughter. Ray runs at the vehicle, but it's
a hopeless gesture. The car heads for the half-open gates, smashes through
and disappears into the night. Ray is left standing in the dust.*

{SCENE 94   INT./EXT. RAY'S FOUR-WHEEL-DRIVE – THE
DESERT. NIGHT.

*Tjulpu watches the receding lights of Wala Wala through the back
window. Already he is brighter, the force of life back in him.
Notwithstanding this, his rigid knuckles cling to the doorhandle as the
vehicle pitches and rocks over the uneven surface.*

TJULPU: Nguyulu wiyana pulkara mingkuringu ngurra palaku.
    Malpu yutulu. ['I didn't like that place much. Too many ghosts.']}

SCENE 95   EXT. THE POLICE COMPOUND – WALA WALA.
NIGHT.   {97}

Ray turns and sees Billy, himself now secured in the lock-up.

BILLY: [*tentatively*] He been … He been hangin', boss …

    Ray walks over to him.

He been hangin'. I didn't … I didn't mean …

    *Ray punches him through the bars. Billy staggers back and falls.
    Ray tries to kick him by putting his leg through, but connects
    only once.*

RAY: You fuckin' idiot! You fuckin' … fuckin' idiot!

    *Ray heads back to the station. Billy drags himself up. He looks at
    the cold, unfriendly cell, and at last at the noose hanging from
    the mesh.*

BILLY: Ray?

Silence. He looks into the corner. The cowboy boot lies on the concrete floor. Billy's eyes widen. The full horror of his situation starts to dawn.

Ray?

SCENE 96   EXT. WALA WALA. MORNING.   {98}

Ray waits impatiently outside the compound in the early morning light as two police Toyotas thunder through the settlement, {watched by hostile eyes}. The vehicles pull up and Ray shakes hands familiarly with the uniformed driver of the first.

RAY: Hi, Tom. Thanks for coming.
TOM: Spot of bother, mate?

> *A light police aircraft shoots overhead and settles onto the bumpy dirt airstrip. Ray looks over at it, suddenly apprehensive, and looks again at Tom. Ray withdraws his hand, sensing betrayal.*

RAY: [*indicating the plane*] What's going on?

SCENE 97   EXT. THE DESERT. MORNING.   {99}

(Note: the filmed scene contains some changes.) David and Tjulpu crouch in the shade of a rocky outcrop. David's vehicle waits at a little distance. Mannga and Poppy are competing with spears, trying to hit a stick jammed in the dirt several metres away. Both are frighteningly accurate.

TJULPU: [*to David*] Nganana malaku yanku ngayku ngurrarakutu.
  ['We'll go back to my country.']
DAVID: Yuwa. Better for you.
POPPY: You too.

> *David looks at him inquiringly. Poppy crosses his wrists.*

You stay: politpalla put you this one. Take you Alice Springs.
DAVID: Me? Why?
POPPY: [*pointing at Tjulpu*] You help him, eh?
DAVID: No, they don't know I help him.

POPPY: Someone tell 'em.
DAVID: Someone tell them?
POPPY: Yuwa.

> *The two old men pause in their game. The conversation has taken a surreal turn. A sudden weight has registered in David's stomach.*

DAVID: Poppy, I can't live in the desert.

> *Poppy draws a circle in the dirt with the tip of his spear.*

POPPY: This one our camp. You little fella, you sleep here.

> *Poppy takes a few paces and draws another circle.*

POPPY: That one watpalla camp.

> *He crosses to a point midway between.*

[*drawing a line between the two camps*] You been put your camp here.

> *Poppy goes back to his circle.*

We waiting, waiting, waiting, you don't come back. [*Indicating Tjulpu, stabbing the Aboriginal circle with the spear*] This one teach you put your camp back here.

> *Poppy places Mannga's spear in David's hands. David handles it like something from another world.*

DAVID: Poppy ...
POPPY: You: watpalla, blackpalla?
DAVID: I'll die out there.

> *Poppy crosses to the midpoint line and obliterates it.*

POPPY: No middle road.

SCENE 98   INT. THE OFFICE – THE POLICE STATION. DAY.
{100}

Senior Sergeant Warren Oaks, C.I.B., sits with his feet up on Ray's desk thumbing through a copy of the Centralian Advocate. *Ray stands on the other side, frustrated and eager to get going, listening to the quiet flip, flip of the pages. Pause.*

OAKS: Yes ... Not really ... ideal. Seen this?

> *Ray takes the paper. On page three is the photograph of Tjulpu and a story: 'Desert Wanderer in Jail'. Ray scans it without interest.*

RAY: Um ... sir ... about the search ...

OAKS: I can't see the need for it, constable.

RAY: Why not?

OAKS: Because there's no evidence of a crime. You need a crime to convict a felon and I have yet to see one.

RAY: But ...

OAKS: I know that you blokes in uniform don't think much of us at C.I.B., but you might have called us. We're not complete fuckwits. We do know how to get a statement from a witness, which is more than you, apparently. Now ... I have been here only a short time, but I have obtained a statement from the doctor and her diagnosis is that your Mr McKay died of a heart attack.

> *Ray snorts.*

Is that funny?

RAY: But, sir ...

OAKS: Have a medical degree as well, do you, constable?

> *Pause.*

I've put out a bulletin for Mr Müller and Mr Tjangala to say they're wanted for questioning; in the meantime that body is going back to Alice, and if the Coroner tells me there's no evidence he was killed, then as far as I'm concerned, he wasn't. Did you really have to put it in the freezer, by the way?

RAY: Sir ... the blacks have a way of killing people that ... that doesn't *leave* any marks.

OAKS: Do they? How interesting. I'm sure a jury will race to convict on that piece of testimony.

RAY: One interview would get it out of him. He doesn't know anything about white law.

OAKS: You better pray he doesn't.

RAY: That's why we have to do a search.

OAKS: He'll turn up at another settlement.

RAY: David will, but Tjulpu won't. He's spent his whole life in the desert.

OAKS: Constable, you're telling me fairy stories. Nobody lives in the desert any more.

RAY: There aren't many, sir, but —

OAKS: [*interrupting*] There are none.

RAY: Sir —

OAKS: [*interrupting*] Constable ... I think you've done enough, don't you?

In the silence they hear, for the first time, a plaintive call from outside.

BILLY: [*out of view*] Raaay ...

Oaks looks toward the sound.

[*out of view*] Ray?

OAKS: Who's that?

RAY: Billy Curlew, sir.

OAKS: The blacktracker?

RAY: Sir.

OAKS: What the fuck is he doing in the lock-up?

RAY: Teach him to pay attention.

OAKS: The man is not a dog, constable.

RAY: No, sir. Dogs are smarter.

Oaks stares at him.

OAKS: This is not your private fiefdom, constable. When you throw the rule book on the shit heap, in the end you always wind up under it. Do you really think that waving a shotgun at a crowd is appropriate bloody behaviour?

Ray is struck dumb.

Oh, you did well. You're going to be a bloody film star, did you know that? They got you on tape, Sunshine. That'll help the inquest, won't it? Into your conduct. I could lay criminal charges right now, just on the basis of that. You're coming back with us, I'm afraid, constable. Now ... release that man.

SCENE 99   INT. THE MUSTER ROOM – THE POLICE
STATION. DAY.   {101}

Ray walks through the muster room clutching the keys to the lock-up. A few uniforms look up from what they're doing. Among them is his mate Tom. Ray hesitates, then gives him the keys.

RAY: Release that bloke, will you?
TOM: Sure.

   Tom is about to go, but Ray seems to have more on his mind.

RAY: Can I take your car for a tick?
TOM: Sure. What's up?
RAY: I need to pick up a witness.

SCENE 100   INT. THE STORE ROOM – THE POLICE
STATION. DAY.   {102}

Ray unlocks the weapons store and breaks out his shotgun.

SCENE 101   INT./ EXT. THE POLICE COMPOUND – WALA
WALA. DAY.   {103}

Carrying the shotgun as discreetly as possible, Ray walks out of the station. Billy is a khaki lump in the corner of the lock-up. Ray watches from a distance as Tom unlocks the door and goes in. Billy is drawn, shaken, almost unrecognisable. Tom is shocked.

TOM: You right?
BILLY: I didn't ... I didn't mean to let 'im go. He was hangin'. He
   was hangin' ...

   Tom stares at him. Billy catches sight of the retreating figure of Ray.

He don't like me no more. Don't like me. I been poor bloody
fella now.

SCENE 102   EXT. A SPINIFEX PLAIN – THE DESERT. DAY.
                                                                {104}

(Note: the filmed scene contains some differences.) David and Tjulpu

trudge across the red-brown spinifex plain. David is already thirsty and tired. He takes a swig from a water bottle.

TJULPU: [*pointing*] Walpa pitjangu. ['Wind coming.']
DAVID: Big wind?
TJULPU: Yuwa ngayuku kutalu, palunya pitjala kirruganlku nganapa tjamana mungawinki. ['Yeah, my brother. He'll come and cover our tracks tomorrow.']

    David tries to make out what Tjulpu has seen, but can't.

SCENE 103   INT./EXT. TOM'S FOUR-WHEEL-DRIVE –
DUNES. DAY.   {105}

Ray hammers his borrowed vehicle over the rolling dunes. He calculates the likely direction of their journey on a well-used topographical map which lies on the seat beside him. The radio crackles to life.

OAKS: [*voice over*] Wala Wala Station to Wala Wala Mobile, over.

    Two waterholes are marked on the map by hand. Ray's finger traces the easiest journey to the nearest of these.

[*voice over*] Wala Wala Station to Wala Wala Mobile, over.

    Ray glances at the radio.

[*voice over*] Constable, this is Senior Sergeant Warren Oaks. Would you mind telling me your position, over?

    Ray stares into the distance, intent only on his quarry.

SCENE 104   EXT. A SMALL ROCKY OUTCROP – THE
DESERT. DAY.   {106}

A clump of spinifex, tied to the end of a spear, plunges into a rock crevice. A surprising length disappears. When rapidly withdrawn it brings up a trickle of water, which drains into a little depression dug nearby. Tjulpu repeats the exercise, then drinks the water. They have arrived at a little rocky outcrop amid some irregular hills. David finally arrives, throat sticky, legs aching, feet burning, and plumps himself down. Suddenly he realises what Tjulpu is doing.

DAVID: Oh, shit.

> *Tjulpu grins broadly as David crawls over to the water, burning his hands on the rocks as he sucks up a few drops. Once more Tjulpu puts his spear down the crevice. This time with the water comes the carcass of a small bird which plops into David's cupped hands. David drops the thing in disgust. Tjulpu laughs raucously. Tjulpu brings up more water and David forces himself to drink. Tjulpu {chews ruminatively on mulbo, a fungus which is acceptable bush food, as he} settles down to work on two pieces of feathered emu skin. What he is making is not too clear. David looks at the tiny corpse, seduced to its death by the fragrance of water. Suddenly Tjulpu cocks his head to listen.*

{SCENE 105   INT./EXT. TOM'S FOUR-WHEEL-DRIVE – THE SPINIFEX PLAIN. DAY.

The engine roars as Ray urges his vehicle on.}

SCENE 106   EXT. THE SMALL ROCKY OUTCROP – THE DESERT. DAY.   {107}

David burps and chokes down a wave of nausea as Tjulpu tugs his shoes off and puts them onto his own feet. He has some difficulty with the laces. David watches, bemused.

DAVID: No, no. Ngayuku tjamana nyunnga. Wiya nyuntupa pirinypa. ['My feet are soft. Not like yours.']

> *David puts a bare foot onto the rock and draws it away sharply.*

Ah ... shit.

TJULPU: [*holding up the feathered skins*] Ngayulu nyuntunya ngaanya kutjunatana yungku. Nyuntu puya pirinypa yanku ngaaku. ['I'll give you these instead. You'll walk like smoke in these.']

Tjulpu stands in the unfamiliar leather. He doesn't have time to consider the strange feeling, however. He sets off at a brisk pace.

DAVID: Hey! Wait up.

TJULPU: [*pointing towards distant hills*] Nyuntu yarra palawana. Ngayulu ngurringkuna nyuntupa ngula. ['You go that way. I'll find you later.']

DAVID: No ... Tjulpu ... Ngayulu wiyana yanku ngayulu wiyanatju waltjalu yantayantanlku ngaaku. ['I can't walk. I can't look after myself out here.']

TJULPU: {[*pointing*] Nyuntu yanku tali palakutu. Ngayulu ngurrikunaku nyuntupa mungawinki. ['You go to those hills. I'll find you in the morning.']} [*Pointing back the way they've come*] Toy-o-ta.

David looks into the distance and finally makes out a tiny plume of red dust. He looks back and Tjulpu is already putting distance between them. Heart thumping, he takes up the feathered shoes.

SCENE 107   EXT. WALA WALA. DAY.   {108}

Sergeant Cameron watches Oaks walk slowly around the two police vehicles. All eight tyres have been slashed. Oaks looks around at the settlement, which might as well be deserted.

OAKS: Shit.

Another three vehicles packed with Aboriginal people drive past. It's been going on all afternoon. He looks at Cameron.

Where are they all going?

CAMERON: Dunno, sir. Be just like 'em to clear out now we built the bloody place for 'em.

Oaks glances at him, vaguely annoyed.

SCENE 108   INT. THE LIVING ROOM – THE DOCTOR'S RESIDENCE. DAY.   {109}

With sudden violence Charlie rips his dreaming map from the wall.

CHARLIE: That fucking maniac out there has wasted two years of my work.

He puts the map on his desk and smooths out imaginary wrinkles. Sarah stares at him and looks down at the forms in front of her: medical supply requisitions.

Margaret's written to me; there's a lectureship going at New South.

Sarah continues to stare at the forms. {None of the quantities have been filled in.}

SARAH: Oh.
CHARLIE: Is that all?
SARAH: You're leaving.
CHARLIE: Well, I can't hang round out here. There's ...

Sarah stares at him and his resolve crumbles. Today is not the day to break up.

Do you want to come?
SARAH: Just like that.

Pause.

Charlie ... what do you want? Do you want to go back to Margaret? I've been left before, you know; I won't ... What do you want?
CHARLIE: I don't know!
SARAH: *Why* don't you know? *Why?* Oh, I forgot. You're an anthropologist: you don't make judgements, you don't act, you don't bring anything to anything.
CHARLIE: No, of course. I should be more like Ray.

She considers him.

SARAH: No. Maybe not.
CHARLIE: [*bitterly*] Yes, I think maybe so.

Sarah doesn't answer.

SCENE 109   EXT. THE DESERT. DAY.   {114}

The First and Second Man watch intently as Poppy takes a handful of sand. He smiles at them mischievously and blows across his palm.

SCENE 110   EXT. THE SMALL ROCKY OUTCROP – THE DESERT. DAY.   {110}

A tiny breeze disturbs the dust around the dead bird, now dry and surrounded by ants. Ray takes a wet handkerchief from the business end of his shotgun and squeezes it into his mouth. The desert is strangely quiet. He examines the ground around the waterhole. His Toyota is parked a little distance away on the sloping ground. Ray finds two sets of tracks heading off together: one David's boots, one bare feet. The radio shatters the silence.

OAKS: [*voice over*] Wala Wala Station to Wala Wala Mobile, over ... Wala Wala Station to Wala Wala Mobile, over.

> *Ray glances up at the angle of the sun: the shadows are starting to lengthen. A blustery wind begins to tug at his hair.*

[*voice over*] Constable, pick up the handset. It'll be dark soon; we'll lose contact.

> *For the first time Ray glances at the radio.*

[*voice over*] Constable, if you pick up that handset ... if you return that vehicle *immediately*, right now ... there may be a chance you will remain in the force. If you do not ... you will be out. Do {you understand? They will throw you to the lions. And in my view ... it's no more than you deserve.}

> *Ray {stares at the tracks, then at the radio. The hissing silence drags on. At last he} reaches out and turns off the radio. He grabs the shotgun from its brace, takes a handful of cartridges from a box on the passenger seat, a water bottle, and sets off into the desert after his quarry.*

> *Some distance away, behind a spinifex bush, Tjulpu has been watching. Around his neck are David's shoes, tied together by the laces.*

SCENE 111   ROCKY HILL COUNTRY – THE DESERT. DAY.
{112}

David rests under a skinny corkwood tree. Around him the wind scampers over hard earth and meagre vegetation. He gingerly touches his blistered toes, peeking out from the sides of the feathered emu shoes. As he looks up he meets the yellow eyes of a lone dingo. After a moment he stands and hobbles on. In the feathered shoes his feet leave no tracks.

SCENE 112   EXT. SAND DUNES – THE DESERT. DUSK. {111}

Ray follows two clear sets of tracks in the failing light, frantic to reach his quarry before nightfall: one left by David's shoes, one by Tjulpu's feet. The wind is now quite strong and he shields his eyes from the sand. Abruptly the tracks finish. Ray looks about, but there's no trace. It is as though they grew wings and flew. He takes a step backwards, another ... then stops. Like the tracks he is following, his own footprints seem to be two sets which both go forward and abruptly stop. He stares back the way he's come.

RAY: Fuck!

He sprints back towards his vehicle.

SCENE 113   EXT. THE SMALL ROCKY OUTCROP – THE DESERT. DUSK.
{113}

The sky is almost black. Ray battles a stiff wind as, gasping, he arrives back at his Toyota. It takes him only a moment to realise that all the tyres have been let down. On the passenger seat the box of cartridges is missing. He looks around, suspecting he is being watched, but can see no one. He rests in the dirt for a moment and takes a swig from his water bottle. He panics that he may have taken too much and checks the level. At last he drags himself up and grabs a backpack.

SCENE 114   EXT. ROCKY HILLS – THE DESERT. NIGHT. {115}

David is at the end of his strength. The murky wind is ferocious. He lurches on across the stony ground, dizzy from hunger, fatigue and dehydration. Feeling his way along a rock wall, at last he crumbles to his knees near a crevice and huddles into it. All is dark. He feels another presence and looks up as a dingo quietly noses round him. It silently bares its teeth: a jagged grey ridge against the blackness. David pushes the creature away and it is swallowed by the stinging sand. David closes his eyes. Soundlessly a hand brushes his face. He opens his eyes to find a human figure squatting at a little distance in the wind.

DAVID: Tjulpu?

> *It's not Tjulpu; it might be the First Man. The figure moves out of sight. David doesn't pause to consider how he can see this figure in the inky dark; he struggles from his uncomfortable shelter and follows.*

SCENE 115   EXT. THE DESERT. NIGHT.   {116}

(Note: in the filmed scene the ghost chases Ray into the lock-up where Danny's boot lies on the floor.)

{*Ray checks his bearings on a compass and adjusts his direction.*} *The beam of Ray's torch moves like a blade as he fights through the dark. He carries his shotgun, some water, food and an HF radio strapped to his back. His eyes, nose and mouth are covered against the sand. Suddenly, against all logic, his torch beam finds tracks in the dirt: a boot, and a moment later, a bare foot. He quickens his pace. The tracks become clearer: he must be only metres away from his quarry; any moment they will loom out of the searing blizzard. Then suddenly he realises they are the tracks of one man: one boot, one bare foot. At that moment the beam of his light picks up the feet of the man: jeans cover the legs, one foot is bare, on the other an intricately tooled cowboy boot. The beam travels up the body as the man turns. The face is that of the Second Man. Suddenly the man's eyes roll upwards and he pokes out his tongue, which seems impossibly swollen and black. Ray cries out. The cloth around his nose and mouth are suffocating him and he tears them off. There is a rope around the neck of the Second Man. He's not standing at all, but slowly revolving on the end of the rope. Ray sees an arm reaching out for him and, in blind terror, raises his shotgun and fires. {The body jerks with each blast, bleeds, but still holds onto life.} Once more the hand reaches out. Ray backs away. The hanging body follows. {Ray makes a mad lunge towards it and the body moves away, always just out of reach. The wind roaring around him, Ray's eyes are drawn to the swollen tongue.} His own mouth opens wide as he screams and fires again.*

SCENE 116   EXT. A WATERHOLE AND GULLY – THE
DESERT. DAY.   {117}

(Note: due to the location, the filmed scene contains some differences.) The silence of nature: birds, the rustle of leaves. It is morning at the sheltered waterhole, and David lies asleep, one hand trailing in the water. It is as though, after his ordeal, he has stumbled into a new, magical world. He is dirty, his feet are swollen, the vestiges of his feathered shoes still clinging to them. The barrel of Ray's shotgun nuzzles his ear. He stirs, tries to push the thing away, suddenly realises what it is and jerks awake. All Ray's experiences during the night are written on his face and body. He looks exhausted and only two-thirds sane. His backpack radio lies a little distance away.

DAVID: Ra —

> *David's throat catches and he dissolves into a fit of coughing. Ray takes in David's appearance as he waits for it to subside.*

RAY: Where is he?

> *David stares at him, momentarily unsure that this is not another vision.*

DAVID: Ray?
RAY: Where is he?

> *David stares at him stupidly. Ray goes down to the water's edge and kneels.*

You're a fuckin' white man, Dave. Fuckin' white man.

> *He leans forward and drinks {blackfella style, dipping his face in the water,} then leans back on his haunches.*

I got more blackfella in me than you'll ever have. That's how I
know you couldn't find this place by yourself. So I'm gunna ask
you once more: where is he?

DAVID: I don't know, {Ray.}

RAY: [*pointing the gun at him*] Bullshit!

DAVID: {I don't!} I don't! I ... don't know how I found this place.

RAY: Bullshit!

DAVID: A man, a spirit ... showed me and —

RAY: [*interrupting*] No ...

DAVID: It was! He touched my face ...

RAY: No! No! No! Don't give me that. Don't give me that spooky
Aboriginal bullshit.

> *David watches him, for the first time really scared.*

{RAY: [*nastily*] I don't want to know.}

> *Ray {glares at their enchanted surroundings, then} looks at his
> reflection in the limpid waterhole. The hanged man stares
> quietly back. David sees a chance and lunges for Ray's gun, but
> he's weak and sore, and Ray handles himself well. He plants a
> foot into David's solar plexus. David doubles up in agony and
> Ray puts the shotgun against his temple.*

RAY: If I blew your fuckin' head off, who would know, eh?

DAVID: [*hoarsely*] Ray ... it's the truth.

> *David squeezes his eyes shut. Pause. Ray lowers the gun.*

RAY: It's okay, Dave. I'm not a killer.

> *He settles next to David, {cocks the shotgun and shows him the
> empty chamber. He's out of ammunition.}*

Thing is ... you think I'm the villain, you know. But I'm not.
I'm just a bloke that ... wants to do his job. Poppy's the villain,
getting people into the ... the blackfella way, the old way,
try'n'a drag it all out when a clean break is what they need. It's
being caught in the *middle*'t fucks you up. When my dad was in
the force ... he used to go into the settlements with the
Protection Board blokes and take the kids away. Just take 'em
away so they never knew about their Dreaming or their

culture. And you know what? I reckon there's value in that. There's value in it.

Ray looks in the water again. The hanged man looks back.

I don't hate Aboriginal people, Dave. Just the opposite. {Just the opposite.}

Both men suddenly react to a sound that echoes eerily along the gully.

TJULPU: [*out of view, singing*] Larrpitupi! Yinka, mantarringu, palunyalukula wakamarra kulatangka. ['Shit! Sing, laugh, he's the one we're going to spear.']

Ray and David stare at one another: is it real or magical? Ray breaks the spell.

RAY: That's him.

Ray stands.

DAVID: Ray ...

RAY: What? He's coming back with me.

Ray moves towards the source of the sound. David hobbles behind.

TJULPU: [*out of view, singing*] Yinka, yinka! Wantiyirralalaka ngananpa kulata yankutjaku parrpakutjaku, parrawitjanjaku larrpitupi! Yinka! ['Sing, sing! Let all our spears go flying, spinning. Shit! Sing!']

As they proceed the rock walls around them begin to narrow. The song seems to be coming from high up one side of the gully. Ray clambers upwards at a pace that David cannot match. Suddenly Tjulpu appears, spear raised.

Yinka, yinka! Wantiyirralalaka ngananpa kulata yankutjaku parrpakutjaku, parrawirrtjaku. Larrapitu! Yinka! ['Sing, sing! Let all our spears go flying, spinning. Shit! Sing!']

RAY: Well, well.

{*Ray takes his handcuffs and tosses them to Tjulpu.*

Nyuntu karrpipa ngaanyanata tjunipa nyuntula minangka. ['You put these handcuffs round your wrists.']}

Tjulpu rattles his spear in his woomera. Ray makes a show of taking careful aim. Suddenly a second spear passes through his left arm, knocking the shotgun from his hands. It has come from the other side of the gully. Ray pitches forward as the shotgun slides down the slope. Tjulpu has disappeared, although his laugh can be heard. David stares in horror as Ray tries to regain his balance with the spear impaling his arm. {From the other side of the gully comes singing.

MANNGA: [*out of view, singing*] Larrpitupi! Yinka, mantarringu, palunyalukula wakamarra kulatangka. ['Shit! Sing, laugh, he's the one we're going to spear.']

Tjulpu joins in.

MANNGA & TJULPU: [*out of view, singing, faintly*] Yinka, yinka! Wantiyirralalaka ngananpa kulata yankutjaku parrpakutjaku, parrawitjanjaku larrpitupi! Yinka! ['Sing, sing! Let all our spears go flying, spinning. Shit! Sing!']}

Ray snaps the end of the spear under his boot and draws it out of his arm.

RAY: Dave?
DAVID: Ray, let me talk to them. [*Calling*] Mannga!
RAY: No, fuck it.

Ray {lurches down the slope and retrieves his shotgun. A rock sails out of nowhere. Ray dodges it,} loses his footing and rolls down the slope. Bruised and battered, Ray finds himself lying in a metre of water at the bottom of the slope. He staggers upright and stares along the gully. At the very end Poppy sits as though enthroned. They stare at each other wordlessly.

DAVID: Ray!
RAY: [*softly*] I think more better this one, eh?

Ray wades along the gully towards Poppy. Stumbling on his damaged feet, David struggles down the slope and into the water.

DAVID: Poppy! {It's empty!} Don't spear him! {Shotgun finish! Shotgun finish!}

He thrashes towards Ray, {who takes hold of the shotgun by the barrel, preparing to use it as a club.} Mannga and Tjulpu leap out from their hiding places and skitter down the slope, spears raised high. As Mannga and Tjulpu approach through the water, Ray tries to face them down, but it's no contest. Mannga feints, Tjulpu's spear flies out and pierces Ray in the side. His blood flows into the water. Ray thrashes about, staring at the long spear emerging from his body. {Even so, he tries once more to strike a blow with the shotgun.} Mannga grasps the end of the spear and, with a practiced gesture, twists it and draws it out. Ray screams and faints. Poppy stands. Mannga and Tjulpu watch unmoved as Ray slips underneath the shallow water. Mannga prepares to administer the coup de grâce. *David finally reaches them and throws himself across Ray, supporting his head out of the water. {Ray coughs and gasps, disoriented and semiconscious.}*

DAVID: [*to Mannga and Tjulpu*] No! Enough!

MANNGA: Finish that one.

DAVID: No. Not finish. Enough. [*Calling along the gully*] Poppy, enough. Spear him, you spear me too.

{*Poppy descends from his throne and wades towards them.*}

TJULPU: [*angrily*] Pungkulala palunya yarra. Palunyaku kututu puli pirinypa. ['Let's kill him and go. His heart is like a stone.']

POPPY: [*to David*] Tjatu nyuntu mukunypa? ['Where is your anger?'] You: blackpalla, watpalla?

David stares at him.

DAVID: I'm just a fella.

Poppy, Mannga and Tjulpu stare at him.

SCENE 117   INT. THE BACK ROOM – THE TEACHER'S
RESIDENCE. DAY.   {118, 119}

(Note: the filmed television item contains some differences.) A video image of the waterhole as Ray is lifted onto a stretcher by Sarah and Billy. Two policemen carry him to a waiting vehicle, Sarah and Billy following. Billy is clearly distressed. The images are on the Mathiesens' television set, at the back of their house.

GORDON: [*voice over*] ... Senior Sergeant Oaks said the constable then ignored instructions and pursued the two men into the desert.

A brief shot of David, looking blank and exhausted, being given a mug of something hot. The Mathiesens' room is revealed. It's empty. The television cuts to Senior Sergeant Warren Oaks.

OAKS: Yes, the officer will be facing disciplinary procedures when, er ... he's sufficiently recovered.

GORDON: [*voice over*] Will action be taken against the Aboriginal men?

SCENE 118   INT. THE LIVING ROOM – THE TEACHER'S
RESIDENCE. DAY.   {119}

(Note: the filmed scene is a montage which moves outside to establish the abandoned settlement.) The television continues indistinctly in the other room. The house has clearly been abandoned. A few school books lie about, pieces of crockery and art, a pile of clothes that were too much to carry at the last minute.

OAKS: [*voice over*] Ah ... We're seeking them for questioning.

GORDON: [*voice over*] And ... will you detain them in custody?

Oaks' annoyance is signalled by the slightest pause.

OAKS: {[*voice over*]} They'll receive the same treatment as any other Australian citizen under Australian law.

SCENE 119   INT. THE BACK ROOM – THE TEACHER'S
RESIDENCE. DAY.   {119, 120}

The television shows Ray being loaded into the back of Sarah's medical vehicle. Ray reaches out for her and she takes his hand. Suddenly the power goes off. An air conditioner winds down slowly. A blustery wind beats about the house.

SCENE 120   EXT. THE AIRSTRIP – WALA WALA. DAY.   {121}

Les, Kate, Adrian, Sonia and Charlie wait for the plane. A wind sock blows fitfully amid the sand. Les stands with an arm about each of the children, keeping them out of reach of Kate. Charlie examines his Dreaming map with minute curiosity. All are buffeted by sand. Sarah is nowhere to be seen. {In the middle distance the police vehicles can be made out near the station. There is no trace of the community that was there a week ago.} Suddenly Charlie releases his map. He watches until it is just another piece of rubbish blowing around the settlement.

CHARLIE: God, what a place.

> *Kate stares at her feet as they are gradually buried by orange sand. Dissolve to:*

SCENE 121   EXT. THE DESERT. DAY.   {122}

(Note: the filmed scene contains some differences.) The sand blows past, clears, the wind settles into silence. Poppy's spell has finally run its course. Poppy, the First and Second Man are all seated over their abandoned card game in the shade of their corkwood tree, as at the opening of the story. It is now late in the day, the temperature is dropping, it's been quite a tale. They stand and stretch. Poppy gathers his cards. They raise a friendly hand to each other and walk off in their separate directions. Poppy turns towards a brand new Toyota four-wheel-drive. He taps it with familiar satisfaction before he opens the driver's door. The Second Man turns back to him.

SECOND MAN: [*crossing his wrists*] Eh: politpalla find you, put you this one?

> *Poppy laughs.*

POPPY: No, I been witness. I don't do nothing.

> *The First and Second Man laugh and continue on their journeys. Poppy gets into his vehicle, starts it and, very inexpertly, drives away. The vehicle bobs and weaves, rarely changing out of second gear, however even at this pace it is gradually swallowed by distance.*

THE END

Film End Credits

CAST

Ray BRYAN BROWN / David ERNIE DINGO / Kate ANGIE MILLIKEN / Tony AARON PEDERSEN / Les LEWIS FITZ-GERALD / Poppy GNARNAYARRAHE WAITAIRE / Bill LAFE CHARLTON / Sarah ANNE TENNEY / Charlie JOHN JARRATT / Mannga PETER FRANCIS / Tjulpu DJUNAWONG STANLEY MIRINDO / Gordon BERYNN SCHWERDT / Farrelly STEVE RODGERS / Sgt. Oaks MARSHALL NAPIER / 2nd Man DAVID GULPILIL / 1st Man BILLY McPHERSON / Tom Erhart ROBERT FAGGETTER / Sonia COURTNEE SPESSOT / Adrian MAX SPESSOT / Benson WESLEY PATTEN / Andrew LARRY GURRUWIWI / Justin DAVID McCORMACK / Painted Man GREGORY WAYNE / Girl At Fence BIANCA TURNER

CREW

Production Manager LESLEY PARKER / 1st Assistant Director JAMIE CROOKS / Production Co-ordinator TRISH FOREMAN / Production Secretary JANE HEALY / Production/Unit Runner TIM FAULKNER / Location Manager MASON CURTIS / Production Accountant CAROLYN JONES MONEYPENNY SERVICES / Continuity SUE WILEY / 2nd Assistant Director ADAM SPENCER / 3rd Assistant Director KATE TURNER / Focus Puller DAMIAN WYVILL / Clapper/Loader MARGARET McCLYMONT / Sound Recordist PHIL TIPENE / Boom Operator MARK PILLEY / Gaffer NICK PAYNE / Best Boy ANTONY TULLOCH / 3rd Electrics GREG DE MARIGNY / Key Grip PAUL THOMPSON / Grip BENN HYDE / Assistant Grip GUY BOWDEN / Costume Supervisor TRACEY RICHARDSON / Stand-by Costume NEVILLE KERR / Assistant Costume FIONA HOLLEY / Make-up/Hair Artists JOSE PEREZ PAUL PATTISON / Art Director RICHARD HOBBS / Set Decorators BRIAN DUSTING SUE MAYBURY / Props Master IGOR LAZAREFF / Construction Managers LARRY SANDY PATRICK THOMPSON / Scenic Artist DAVID TUCKWELL / Art Department Buyer/Dresser/Runner ANDREW ROBILLARD / Stand-by Carpenter MURRAY SIMMANCE / Draughtsperson AXL BARTZ / Greens Department

PETER HORDERN MATTHEW JAMES / Decorator's Assistant –
Alice Springs SAMANTHA WARD / Construction Assistant – Alice
Springs ASHLEY HOLT / Construction Assistant – Sydney DOUGAL
THOMPSON / Armourers PAUL TURKINGTON PARADOX FX
PETER COGAR / Extra Casting KRIS WALLIS / Casting Assistant
KRISTIN WHITFIELD / Unit Stills Photographer LISA TOMASETTI
/ Unit Publicist TRACEY MAIR / Publicist MARIA FARMER /
Caterer STEVE MARCUS / Assistant Caterer TIM KAU /
Unit/Location STEVE SALOTTI / Unit Supervisor/Catering Assistant
DEB HANSON / Facility Driver JIM DAVIDSON / Unit Nurse
JENNY BICHARD / Stunt Co-ordinator WALLY DALTON / Safety
Assistant IAN MALL / Special Effects FILMTRIX PETER STUBBS
JEFF LITTLE ANGELO SAHIN ROB HEGGIE KEVIN TURNER
/ Sacred Sites Consultant BOBBY STUART / Jay Creek Custodian
OOPIE CAMPBELL

ADDITIONAL SYDNEY CREW
Key Grip GEORGE TSOUTAS / Electrics DARRYN FOX
JONATHAN HUGHES GARTH ALLEN PETER HOLLAND /
Post Production Supervisor SYLVIA WALKER WILSON / Post
Production Secretary JANET COOK / Post Production Facility
SOUNDFIRM SYDNEY / Assistant Editor SAM PETTY / Sound
Effects Editor TIM JORDAN / Dialogue Editor JOHN PENDERS /
ADR Editor MAUREEN RODBARD-BEAN / Additional Sound
Editing SAM PETTY ANGUS ROBERTSON / Foley Artists
GERARD LONG MARIO VACCARO / Foley Engineers STEVE
BURGESS SCOTT HEMING / ADR Supervisor TIM JORDAN /
ADR Engineers CATE CAHILL MICHAEL THOMPSON / Sound
Mixer IAN McLOUGHLIN / Assistant Mixer JONATHAN
HEMMING / Mixed at SOUNDFIRM SYDNEY / Laboratory ATLAB
AUSTRALIA / Laboratory Liaison SIMON WICKS IAN RUSSELL /
Negative Matching KERRY FERGUSON / Grading ARTHUR
CAMBRIDGE / Opening Titles Design & Production ANIMAL
LOGIC ANDY BROWN KRISELLE BAKER MELANIE RITCHIE /
End Credits Design & Shooting OPTICAL & GRAPHIC / Music
Produced by GREG WHITE / Choir SYDNEY CHAMBER CHOIR /
Conducted by PHILIP GRIFFIN / Guitar GREG WHITE / Orchestra
Contractor PHILIP HERTL / Didgeridoo Solo Performed by ALAN
DARGIN / Music Consultant CHRISTINE WOODRUFF / Script
Editing JOANNA ARROWSMITH BRYAN BROWN / Travel
Organised by TRAVELTOO GREG HELMERS / Alice Springs
vehicles supplied by HERTZ NORTHERN TERRITORY / Sydney

vehicles supplied by ORANA CAR &TRUCK RENTALS / Cast, Make-up & Wardrobe facilities MASON CURTIS CLARK FILM SERVICES / Freight organised by SHOWFREIGHT FORWARDING SHANE McKECHNIE FILM LINK INTERNATIONAL AUST. LYN QUILTY / Camera equipment supplied by SAMUELSON FILM SERVICE BILL ROSS / Film stock supplied by KODAK AUSTRALIA / Completion Guarantor FILM FINANCES INC. ADRIENNE READ / Insurance H.W. WOOD AUSTRALIA TONY GIBBS / Legal. HART & SPIRA LLOYD HART / Original artwork by JOANNA ARROWSMITH / With Thanks To QANTAS CARLTON UNITED BREWERIES (NSW) PTY LIMITED TOYOTA MOTOR CORPORATION AUSTRALIA LTD PLAZA HOTEL, ALICE SPRINGS, JOHN CLARK and NEIL ARMFIELD.

"Eagle Rock" / Written by ROSS WILSON (Mushroom Music). performed by Daddy Cool Licensed from Castle Communications (Australia) Limited

All characters and events depicted in this film are fictitious. Any similarity between actual persons living or dead is purely coincidental. This cinematographic film (including the soundtrack thereof) is protected by the copyright laws of Australia and other applicable laws worldwide. Any unauthorised copying, duplication or presentation may incur severe civil and criminal penalties.
This film was developed with the assistance of NSW FILM AND TV OFFICE
Financed by the AUSTRALIAN FILM FINANCE CORPORATION LIMITED
© 1996 Australian Film Finance Corporation Limited and Dead Heart Productions Pty Limited.

SCREENPLAYS FROM CURRENCY PRESS

Strictly Ballroom
Baz Luhrmann and Craig Pearce

The Adventures of Priscilla, Queen of the Desert
Stephan Elliott

Muriel's Wedding
P.J. Hogan

The Sum of Us
David Stevens

Bad Boy Bubby
Rolf de Heer

Cosi
Louis Nowra

Angel Baby
Michael Rymer

Children of the Revolution
Peter Duncan

ALL INQUIRIES TO:
Currency Press,
PO Box 452,
Paddington,
NSW 2021
Tel: 02 9332 1300
Fax: 02 9332 3848
E-mail: currency@magna.com.au
WWW: http://www.currency.com.au